MEDICINE
and
STAMPS

Edited by
R. A. KYLE, M.D. AND M. A. SHAMPO, Ph.D.

Library of Congress Catalog Card Number: 70-112916

© 1970 The American Medical Association

This Edition is a compilation with revisions and addi-
tions of articles on stamps and medicine appearing in
the *Journal of the American Medical Association* during
1961 to 1969, plus new articles specially prepared for
this volume.

Published by The American Medical Association
Printed in United States of America

OP-243   9801-256F; 1-70 10M

FOREWORD

At a meeting of the American Medical Association in Miami in 1960, the late John A. Mirt staged a postage stamp exhibit, entitled "Medical Pathfinders on Stamps." As a result of the interest aroused, during the ensuing years, since July, 1961, more than two hundred biographical vignettes have been used as white space fillers in The Journal of the American Medical Association, illustrated by photographs of stamps.

Publication of a collection of these in book form had been suggested by the steady interest provoked among The Journal's readers. Some vignettes appear here much as prepared by Mr. Mirt, others have been so revised and rewritten by the editors that joint authorship is awarded; many are freshly prepared, and a few appear over the names of other contributors. Dr. Shampo's collection provided most of the stamps illustrated, and a smaller number of illustrations are from Dr. Samuel Bluefarb's material. Authors of the vignettes are identified at the foot of each.

Identification is limited to the numbers to be found in Scott's Standard Postage Stamp Catalogue, where further information on colors, watermarks, papers, perforations, and other philatelic characterization may be found. These reproductions are uniformly magnified slightly more than 25 per cent in dimensions, resulting in a 50 per cent area increase. As a labor of love, great effort has been expended in accuracy of fact presented, but, no claim is made for the information in this volume being either medically or philatelically complete. It has been possible to present only a small part of the ever enlarging field of medical stamps. Many distinguished physicians have never been honored on stamps. Many countries do not portray living persons, leaving the field dominated by the historical past.

Medical and scientific personalities are offered almost exclusively, including such men as Gregor Mendel, not himself a physician, yet whose accomplishments have made a deep imprint. They are presented as nearly as possible in alphabetical order. A listing by stamp-issuing countries replaces a table of contents, and an index shows only the principal scientific or medical fields of activity of the individuals presented.

Although some of the following stamps appear in sets of several values, all with the same imprint, reference is given only to a single stamp, together with its Scott's Catalogue number. Two Brazilian and one French item offer biographies of closely related individuals who do not actually appear on the stamps.*

*The biographical sketches are in alphabetical order except for Guerin who is coupled with Calmette, Vianna coupled with Leishman, and Pirajá da Silva coupled with Manson.

Also, Romay Chacon is shown under "R" ahead of Ramón y Cajal.

TABLE OF CONTENTS
—Listed by country issuing stamps—
Reference is to Scott's Catalogue number.

IX

XI

DEVELOPMENT OF CHILD CARE IN CUBA

Angel Arturo Aballi (1880-1952), Cuban pediatrician, gave a half century of his life to further the cause of medicine in his country and many parts of South America. He not only was a builder but he took a frontline role in the defense of the profession when it came under political attack.

Aballi was born in Matanzas, Cuba, and received his MD degree from the University of Havana in 1901. This was followed by postgraduate studies in the United States and Europe. In 1908, he was placed in charge of the teaching of child psychology at the University of Havana. As Dean of the School of Medicine (1936-1940), he carried on an active campaign against tuberculosis in children and founded child care services and sanitaria.

Pediatrics societies in all parts of the world recognized Aballi's ability by electing him to membership. In many of these, he held offices, including that of president or honorary president. He was a recipient of the coveted Finlay Order award. He directed the publication of Revista Medica Cuba in 1918. Cuba honored him postally (Scott No. 600) in 1958.—Mirt, J. A.

ARABIAN SURGERY

Albucasis, Abulcasis, Abulkasim, Abu-al-Qasim, or by what other short name Abou al Kasseem Khalaf ben Abbas Al Zarahivi (936 - ca. 1013) may be called, was the greatest exponent of the Arabian school of medicine in the 10th century. His *al-Tasrif* ("Collection"), a treatise on medicine and surgery, was the leading textbook on surgery for more than three centuries in the Middle Ages.

Albucasis, born near Cordova in Andalusia, Spain, wrote in Arabic. His al-Tasrif consisted of three books based on the work of Paul of Aegina. There were profuse illustrations of surgical and dental instruments, some of which were of his invention. He emphasized cautery, a feature of Arabic medicine, and mentioned a half hundred diseases which he treated by fire. He described lithotomy, amputations, trephining and many other surgical procedures. His obstetric and gynecologic treatises reflected the custom which prevented men from direct examination of a virgin and called for directions to a female assistant.

A generous portion of his books was devoted to dentistry and oral surgery, to which he contributed many new concepts. His descriptions and instruments placed new emphasis and light on that field. It was for that reason that his portrait was selected to adorn a 60-p. stamp issued by the Syrian Arab Republic (Scott No. C314) in 1964 to commemorate the 4th Arab Congress of Dental and Oral Surgery in Damascus.—Mirt, J. A.

2

VICTIM OF X-RAY
BURN

"Martyr to Medicine" is a fitting epitaph for Alvaro Alvim (1863-1928), Brazilian physician. He received his MD degree from the University of Rio de Janeiro, Brazil, in 1887. The discovery of x-rays in 1895 whetted his appetite, and he went to Paris for study at the St. Louis and the San Antoine hospitals.

Proper safeguards were not set up in the early years of medicine's new weapon against disease. As a result, Alvim's experimental work caused x-ray burns that eventually resulted in the amputation of both hands. Nevertheless, he continued his work with the aid of prostheses until his death. He is thus pictured on a Brazilian postage stamp (Scott No. 971) issued in 1963 to commemorate the centenary of his birth.—Mirt, J. A.

MYTHOLOGY
IN EARLY MEDICINE

Early medical history is so mixed with mythology that it is often difficult to distinguish between them. To the ancient Greeks the god of healing was Asklepios (ca. 1300 B.C.), son of Apollo. The Romans knew him as Aesculapius.

Tradition has it that Asklepios was removed from his mother's womb by Apollo after he had slain her. The child was reportedly placed in care of the centaur Chiron who taught him botany and the effectiveness of plants in healing.

Mythology also suggests that in 1237 B.C., Zeus, irked by Asklepios' proposed revival of the dead, had the latter slain by a bolt of lightning. Later, Zeus relented and elevated Asklepios to the godhead of medicine and placed him among the stars.

An Aesculapian cult developed throughout Greece, and reached Rome in 293 B.C. Thus, Asklepios became the Roman god of healing, a position he held until approximately 500 A.D. For nearly a thousand years the afflicted visited temples erected to him, to be healed by drugs, diet, and other modes of treatment.

"Asclepicia" became in time well staffed health resorts, ornate with art and golden treasures. Rich and poor sought benefits. The staff of Asklepios, entwined by a serpent, became the symbol of medicine, continuing long after his status as deity had subsided. Mythology also credits Asklepios with a daughter, Hygeia, the goddess of health, who assisted him. Asklepios, or his staff, can be seen on the stamps of many countries, as on this Spanish stamp of 1948 (Scott RA 26).—Mirt, J. A.

EYE SURGERY

Great strides were made in eye surgery in Europe in the middle of the 19th century. One of the "pathfinders" in that field was Carl Ferdinand von Arlt (1812-1887), Austrian ophthalmologist, whose work was acclaimed throughout the continent. Born in Teplitz, von Arlt received his MD degree from the University of Prague in 1839. His interest centered on diseases of the eye. He was a professor of ophthalmology at the University of Prague from 1849 to 1856 before moving to a similar appointment at the University of Vienna.

Meanwhile, in 1854, he had become associated with von Græfe of Berlin and Donders of Holland in the publication of *Archiv für Ophthalmologie* which became the repository of reports on medical research into diseases of the eye. Arlt contributed many treatises to this journal based on his surgical activities.

Von Arlt's name is linked with an operation for distichia. The ciliary bulbs are dissected from the tarsus by excision of a crescent-shaped piece of skin and transplanted away from the edge of the lid. "Von Arlt's trachoma" is the granulated form thereof.

Among other procedures introduced by him were operations for enucleation of a diseased or injured eye, the relief of symblepharon, and the repair of strictures of the lacrimal ducts. In 1875, he wrote a tract on the medicolegal aspects of injuries of the eye.

Von Arlt's portrait appears on an Austrian postage stamp (Scott No. B161) issued in 1937.—Mirt, J. A.

5

PERCUSSION SIGNS

Leopold von Auenbrugger (1722-1809) is credited with development of percussion, an important technique in the diagnosis of disease. But, the recognition of his discovery by the medical profession did not come until just before his death, and then after many years of ridicule and disbelief on the part of most of his colleagues.

Auenbrugger was born in Graz, Austria, and educated in medicine at the University of Vienna, where he received his degree in 1752. He was made physician-in-chief of the Holy Ghost Hospital, Vienna. As a boy helper in his father's inn, Auenbrugger had learned that the thumping of barrels gave different sounds, depending on the contents of liquid. He decided to try this technique in medicine. While at the hospital, he found that certain sounds could be heard by tapping the patient's chest. Further research showed that these sounds varied according to diseased conditions. In 1761, Auenbrugger published his *Inventum Novum*. He stated that percussion gave information concerning the size of the heart and the condition of the pleural cavity. This revolutionary theory brought him widespread criticism. He was forced to resign his hospital appointment and went into private practice.

Jean Nicholas Corvisart, favorite physician of Napoleon, produced a French treatise on cardiac disease in which he revived Auenbrugger's theory and gave full credit to the Austrian physician.

A bulging in the epigastic region in the presence of pericardial effusion has been known medically as Auenbrugger's sign. Auenbrugger was honored on an Austrian stamp (Scott No. B157) in 1937.—Mirt, J. A.

ARABIAN PHYSICIAN, VERSATILE SCIENTIST

Avenzoar (1091-1162), born in Cordova, Spain, became one of the great Jewish physicians of the Western Caliphate of the Fatimides. Essentially an empiricist, he was one of the first to oppose Galenism. He was the first to describe scabies, and he also described serous pericarditis, mediastinal abscess, pharyngeal paralysis, and inflammation of the middle ear. In his discussions of treatment, he recommended goat's milk for tuberculosis and after tracheotomy. His best-known work was "Rectification of Health."

He was honored on a stamp (Scott No. C413) issued by the Syrian Arab Republic in 1968.—Shampo, M. A., and Kyle, R. A.

AVICENNA, PRINCE OF PHYSICIANS

Ibn Sina or Avicenna (980-1037), a Persian, has been called the "Prince of Physicians." During the Middle Ages medicine in Persia reached its zenith under his leadership. He was appointed court physician to Nuh ibn-Mansur at 18 and was a great sage as well. His *Canon,* written in Arabic, was a recognized textbook for several hundred years. A fondness for wine, women, and song is blamed for shortening his life.

In the light of today's knowledge, Avicenna contributed to medical progress; however, many of his theories were of questionable value, if not an actual hindrance to the progress of medicine. His *Canon* promulgated to physicians the pernicious idea that the deduction of conclusions from premises is better than first-hand investigation. He also set back surgery by inculcating the novel doctrine that the surgical art is an inferior and separate branch of medicine and by substituting cautery for the knife. Avicenna is said to have been the first to describe the preparation and properties of sulphuric acid and alcohol. Postally, he has been honored many times. Poland honored him by an issue (Scott No. 558) in 1952, on the 1000th anniversary of his birth, and he is shown on a recent issue of the Yemen Arab Republic.—Mirt, J. A.

MIDDLE EUROPEAN PHYSICIAN

Victor Babes (1854-1927), born in Vienna, was graduated from the University of Budapest in 1872, and studied under Virchow and Koch. He described a genus *(Babesia)* of hemosporidia, transmitted by ticks. One species *bigemina* causes Texas fever in cattle. He and P. Ernst described metachromatic granules that readily take up stains in spore-bearing bacteria. He demonstrated the penetration of bacteria through the unbroken skin or mucous membrane, and advocated the treatment of rabies by the injection of spinal cord suspension infected with rabies viruses attenuated by heating. He also prepared an antituberculosis serum and developed the mallein test (skin sensitivity to *M. mallei*) for glanders. His bibliography lists 657 items. He was honored philatelically by Romania (Scott No. 1498) in 1962.—Kyle, R. A., and Shampo, M. A.

MILITARY DISTINCTION AND MEDICINE

Noel Eugene Ballay (1848-1902) was a French physician, the greater part of whose life was devoted to African colonization rather than to medicine. Ballay, a medical graduate of the University of Paris in 1880, joined the navy as a surgeon from which service he was appointed medical officer and health adviser to an expedition into the French Congo.

Ballay was largely instrumental in the formation of the Sengalese French colonies. He served as governor of French Guinea (1891-1900), and was governor of the Sengalese territories when he died of diabetes in 1902. He was honored in 1954 by an issue (Scott No. 61) of French West Africa, although earlier 1906 sets of Dahomey, Senegal, and other French colonies carry his portrait as well. —Mirt, J. A.

ANGEL OF THE BATTLEFIELD

The American Red Cross movement was the brain child of Clara Barton (1821-1912), who administered to the wounded in the Civil War (1861-1865) and the Franco-Prussian War (1870-1871). For her latter service as "Angel of the Battlefield," she was decorated by the German government.

Miss Barton was a "Christmas present" in an old farmhouse in North Oxford, Mass. After the Civil War, President Lincoln gave her the task of identifying the bodies of unknown soldiers. Through her efforts, about 13,000 were identified and returned to bereaved relatives.

In her European services, she had seen the Red Cross in action. She was so impressed that she started a campaign which resulted in the formation of the American Red Cross in 1881. She became its first president, and maintained that position until her death. Under her leadership, Red Cross activities were expanded to provide relief also in floods, earthquakes, famines, epidemics, fires, and other disasters. In 1948, The United States issued a stamp (Scott No. 967) in her honor.—Mirt, J. A.

BÉCLÈRE — RADIOLOGIST

The introduction of radium therapy and x-ray visualization near the end of the 19th century exacted a heavy toll among the medical pioneers. The dangers did not become apparent until the victim had absorbed lethal dosages. Antoine Béclère (1856-1939), who had practiced for more than a decade as a pediatrician, saw the possibilities in the new field with the establishment of proper safeguards.

Béclère set out to become a "pathfinder" and before his death at 83 he had spent two thirds of a 65-year medical career specializing in radiology as a teacher, investigator, and writer.

Béclère was born in Paris, the son of a physician, and received his MD degree from the University of Paris in 1887. He had built up a good pediatric practice when attracted by radiology. In 1907, he reported on the treatment of cancer by x-rays. He also introduced x-rays in the treatment of glandular tuberculosis.

During World War I, he served as chief of physiotherapy at L'Hôpital Val de Grace. In 1921, he joined the Curie Institute in Paris as a professor of radiology. He became president of the French Academy of Medicine in 1928, and three years later served as president of the Third International Congress on Radiology.

Béclère, recipient of the French Legion of Honor, has been recognized internationally. France, in 1957, issued a 12-franc postage stamp (Scott No. 822) bearing his portrait, a fluoroscope, roentgen tube, and the inscription "founder of French radiology."—Mirt, J. A.

FRENCH PHYSICIST — DISCOVERER OF RADIOACTIVITY

Antoine Henri Becquerel (1852-1908), the discoverer of radioactivity, was born Dec. 15, 1852, and graduated from the École Polytechnique. In 1895, he was appointed a professor of physics at the school, where in 1896, he discovered that uranium at ordinary temperatures emitted an invisible radiation which in many respects resembled x-rays and could affect a photographic plate after passing through thin plates of metal. These rays differed from x-rays in that they were deflected by electric or magnetic fields. Originally called Becquerel rays, the phenomenon is now known as *radioactivity* and is recognized as a nuclear property of certain elements. For these researches, he was awarded in 1903 the Rumford Medal of the Royal Society (London), and received a Nobel prize jointly with Pierre and Marie Curie.

He also did work on magnetism, polarization of light, phosphorescence and the absorption of light in crystals. He died at Le Croisic in Brittany on Aug. 25, 1908. He was honored postally by a French stamp (Scott No. B202) issued in 1946.—Shampo, M. A., and Kyle, R. A.

RUSSIAN
NEUROLOGIST

Vladimir Mikhailovich Bekhterev (1857-1927), Russian neurologist, was a "pathfinder" in medicine. A prolific writer, he left a heritage of information concerning neurology, anatomy, pathology, and physiology. He organized scientific societies, institutions, and medical journals to spread his knowledge widely.

In 1892, Bekhterev described chronic arthritis of unknown etiology marked by a progressive deformity, stiffness, and bony fusion of vertebrae, known for a time as Bekhterev's disease, now as rheumatoid spondylitis. His name also is linked with descriptions of a layer of fibers in the cerebral cortex, to a nucleus of the vestibular portion of the auditory nerve, to a reaction in tetany, to a facial reflex or contraction, and to a sign in cases of neurosyphilis and paresis.

Bekhterev was born in an isolated village in Eastern Russia and received his MD degree from the University of St. Petersburg in 1881. He acquired further medical education in Germany and France before being appointed in 1885 to the chair of neurology and psychiatry at the University of Kazan, Russia. Nine years later, he was made a professor at the St. Petersburg (now Kirov) Military Medical Academy. He devoted a goodly portion of his late years to the public health field.

Russia in 1952 issued a postage stamp (Scott No. 1655) to commemorate the 25th anniversary of his death.
—Mirt, J. A.

PIONEER
IN IMMUNOLOGY

Emil von Behring (1854-1917) was born March 15, 1854, at Hansdorf in East Prussia. He was a graduate of the Army Medical School in Berlin in 1878, after which he entered the Army. Iodoform bandages were commonly used at this time, and he became interested in the mode of action showing that iodine was released from iodoform, with a beneficial effect on bacterial products. This was the basis of his idea for therapy of infectious diseases by the use of substances that neutralized the poisons of microbes (antitoxins).

In 1888, Behring studied the serums of white rats that were immune to anthrax and believed that the immunity was due to the alkalinity of the serum. Shortly thereafter, Roux and Yersin reported that diphtheria cultures contained a toxin, and subsequently other investigators showed that a toxin was also present in cultures of the tetanus bacillus. Then von Behring and C. Frankel demonstrated almost simultaneously that animals could be made immune to the diphtheria toxin. Von Behring reported that serums of animals immunized with diphtheria toxin neutralized the toxin, and, in December, 1890 announced this discovery of antitoxin for diphtheria and tetanus. Trials of diphtheria antitoxin were started in 1891, and the antitoxin became available for medical practice in 1894; Roux quickly confirmed its value in clinical practice.

Von Behring became associated with the University of Marburg. In later life, he worked to establish immunity against diphtheria in children by giving them a combination of diphtheria toxin and antitoxin. He also did research in tuberculosis, received the Nobel Prize in Physiology and Medicine in 1901, the first ever awarded. He died of pneumonia March 31, 1917, and was honored by a German issue (Scott Nos. B186-187) in 1940.—Kyle, R. A. and Shampo, M. A.

FROM DRAMA TO PHYSIOLOGY

Many paths in modern physiology start at the laboratory door of Claude Bernard (1813-1878), whose early career as a pharmaceutical assistant was marked by an ambition to be a playwright. Fortunately for medicine, he was urged to give up that ambition by a drama critic who found Bernard's literary work unacceptable.

Bernard became an assistant to François Magendie (1783-1855), French physiologist and pharmacologist, at the Hôtel Dieu in Paris, for whom a chair in general physiology was founded at the Sorbonne in 1854. Four years later, Bernard was appointed to the chair of medicine at the Collège de France. In 1868, he was given a seat in the French Academy, and the next year he entered the senate.

Bernard solved many secrets of life, and coined the term "internal secretion." His methods served as a guidepost to future investigators in the processes of life, death, and disease. He contributed a keystone to modern physiology when he discovered the vasoconstrictor nerves. He demonstrated the glycogenic function of the liver, and the three-fold action of pancreatic juice. He showed that the body performs a physiological synthesis by breaking down chemicals and building up complex substances. His name is associated with "Bernard's duct" or canal (ductus pancreaticus accessorius or the duct of Santorini), "Bernard's layer" (a layer of cells which lines the acini of the pancreas), and "Bernard's puncture" (puncture at a definite point on the floor of the 4th ventricle, causing an artificial diabetes).

He sacrificed his home life for medicine. Bernard's wife and daughters deserted him when he refused to give up experimental medicine for the more lucrative practice of his profession. France issued a stamp (Scott No. B89) in 1939, with the surtax being used for unemployed intellectuals.—Mirt, J. A., Kyle, R. A. and Shampo, M. A.

SWEDISH PHYSICIAN
AND CHEMIST

Jöns Jacob Berzelius (1779-1848) was a Swedish physician but his reputation was established as a chemist. He introduced the modern system of writing chemical symbols and formulas and gave the world an alphabet of chemistry. Thus, he is regarded as the founder of modern inorganic chemistry.

Berzelius was born in Westerlosa, Sweden. He received a degree in chemistry in 1802 and one in medicine from the University of Upsala in 1809, after which he became a professor at the College of Surgery, Stockholm. His research, however, was largely in the field of chemistry. Among his discoveries were the elements selenium, thorium, and cerium. In 1840, he isolated biliverdin, a dark green bile pigment, formed in the body from hemoglobin but largely reduced in the liver to bilirubin, the main pigment of bile. He also described a quantitative test for albumin in urine using acetic acid, and a test for albumin with metaphosphoric acid.

Berzelius served as a professor of medicine at Stockholm University and for 30 years was secretary of the Stockholm Academy of Science. He was honored philatelically by Sweden (Scott Nos. 293, 295, 297) in 1939.
—Mirt, J. A.

ANATOMY AS THE BASIS OF MEDICINE

"No one has done so much and so well in so short a time," said Jean Nicholas Corvisart, surgeon to Napoleon, in speaking of Marie François Xavier Bichat (1771-1802), French surgeon and anatomist. In his short 31 years of life, which encompassed the French Revolution of 1793 and the resultant disorganization of medicine, he laid the foundation for modern histology and histological pathology.

Bichat's philosophy was: "Dissect in anatomy, experiment in physiology, follow the disease and make the necropsy in medicine. This is the threefold path, without which there can be no anatomist, no physiologist, no physician." A good general philosophy even today!

Bichat was born in Thoirette, France, the son of a physician. His education in anatomy and surgery was interrupted by draft into the French Revolutionary Army. The revolution, with its wholesale executions by the guillotine (invented by a French physician, Joseph Ignace Guillotin), provided him with about 600 human bodies. These he dissected meticulously at the Hôtel Dieu, a charity hospital in Paris. The knowledge gained gave him the background for his last great literary work, the five-volume *Anatomie Générale*. Here he gave detailed descriptions of the tissues in healthy and in diseased bodies, establishing him as the founder of modern histology and histopathology. Several anatomical structures in the brain have been named after him.

After the revolution, Bichat became a pupil of Pierre Joseph Desault (1744-1795), physician at the Hôtel Dieu, and at the latter's death was appointed to the vacant post. As the revolution had left medical practice and education in France badly disorganized, Bichat, to correct the situation, formed in 1796 the Société Médicale d'Émulation de

Paris for young doctors to meet in debates.

Tuberculosis and overwork took its toll. Bichat collapsed one day and death came rapidly. By order of Napoleon, a bust of Bichat was placed at the Hôtel Dieu. He is honored on a French stamp (Scott No. B334) issued in 1959, with the surtax going to the Red Cross—Mirt, J. A.

PHYSICIAN
PARASITOLOGIST

Theodor Maximilian Bilharz (1825-1862) was born on March 23, 1825, in Sigmaringen, Germany, and received his MD degree from the University of Tubingen in 1848. In 1850, he left for Cairo, Egypt, where he became first Chief of the Surgical Service and, in 1853, Chief of the Medical Service at the Kast El Aini Hospital and Medical School. In 1856, he became a professor of anatomy, dying six years later at only thirty-seven.

While working in Cairo on several of the prevalent diseases of Egypt, he discovered (1851) the parasitic worm *S. haematobium* the causative agent of schistosomaisis or bilharziasis. The eggs leave the human body, hatch and enter a snail; the larvae emerge and penetrate the skin of man, developing into mature worms in the blood vessels of the liver or bladder, causing cirrhosis, irritability of the bladder, hematuria, and diarrhea. This disease, at first called "Bilharz' Disease" or "Bilharzia," has been a scourge for centuries, in many parts of the earth, and in some areas it still is the cause of more illness than any other single disease. The discovery of the causative organism, a truly pioneer accomplishment, represented one of the greatest advances in medical knowledge. It provided both inspiration and information to those who were then laying the foundation for the great era of progress in bacteriology and parasitology.

Bilharz died in Cairo on May 9, 1862, and was postally honored by the United Arab Republic (Scott No. 122) on the centenary of his death.—Shampo, M. A., and Kyle, R. A.

BILLROTH,
SURGICAL GENIUS

A shining light in the so-called "Second Vienna School," which prevailed in the last half of the 19th century, was Christian Albert Theodor Billroth (1829-1894), a pioneer in abdominal surgery.

Billroth had yearned to become a concert pianist, but he was urged by his mother to take up medicine. He obtained his MD degree in Berlin in 1852, and for a time he taught in Zurich. But in 1867 he became a professor of surgery at the University of Vienna, and served in that capacity a quarter of a century. His clinic became one of the most renowned in Europe.

Seeing the possibilities in surgery, he resorted first to animal experimentation. He performed a total laryngectomy in 1873, after trying out his ideas on a dog. A year later, he excised a urinary bladder tumor and subsequently devised the Billroth I operation for gastric resection, and Billroth II operation for anastomosing the stomach to the jejunum. He also contributed other important techniques to surgery. Billroth was honored by Austria (Scott No. No. B163) in its set of stamps on famous Austrian physicians issued in 1937.—Mirt, J. A.

TEACHER OF MEDICINE

Hermann Boerhaave, clinician and teacher of medicine (1668-1738), was reared in the hope that he would follow in the footsteps of his clerical father. Fortunately for medicine, parental plans were circumvented, and he became the greatest clinician and medical educator of his time. As he was versed in a dozen languages, physicians and medical students came from many lands to attend his classes.

It was not until near the end of the 17th century that Boerhaave gave his attention to medicine. He had previously gone through a period of education in logic, natural philosophy, metaphysics, and ethics—financed by tutoring. Pursuing his study of medicine, he took courses in anatomy, dissection, chemistry, and botany.

Boerhaave received his MD degree from the University of Harderwijk, Holland. In 1701, he went to Leyden, a few miles from his birthplace, and lectured in medicine at the University for eight years. He was then appointed professor of medicine, chemistry, and botany. The latter subject in that period was an important facet in medical education, and Boerhaave developed the Leyden botanical garden into one of the finest in Europe. Among his pupils was Linnaeus, who devised a system of botanical and zoological classification.

A chronic sufferer from gout, many of Boerhaave's writings covered that affliction. The ailment forced him to vacate prematurely his chair at Leyden. Postally, he has been twice honored by the Netherlands. The stamp shown (Scott No. B107) was issued in 1938 on the 200th anniversary of his death.—Mirt, J. A.

STUDENT AND PRACTITIONER OF MEDICINE

Pierre Fidèle Bretonneau (1778-1862), French pathologist and surgeon, was a pathfinder in differentiating a number of diseases. His reports led to remedial measures reducing the mortality rate, especially among children.

In 1814, Bretonneau received his MD degree, 15 years after his graduation as "Officier de Santé." After a brief rural practice, he was appointed Chief of Medicine at the University in Tours in 1815. It was there that he contributed new data on such diseases as typhoid fever and diphtheria. He gave the latter disease its present name. He is credited with performing the first successful tracheotomy for croup (1825). He advocated giving a single large dose of quinine after a paroxysm of malaria.

In 1855, Bretonneau suggested the germ theory of disease, some 20 years before Pasteur announced his important findings. He was honored by France (Scott No. 1022) in 1962 on the centenary of his death.—Mirt, J. A.

DISCOVERY OF CAUSE
OF MALTA FEVER

David Bruce (1855-1931) was born in Melbourne, Australia, on May 29, 1855. Although an indifferent student when he received his basic education in Scotland, he showed an early interest in natural history, and later graduated in medicine from the University of Edinburgh. He joined the Royal Army Medical Corps and was sent to Malta in 1883. Malta (undulant) fever was a serious problem to the residents of the island. Bruce demonstrated an organism, which he called *Micrococcus melitensis,* in the spleens of 10 persons who had died of undulant (Malta) fever in 1886.

Themistocles Zammit (1864-1935) found a positive Widal test reaction in the blood of goats given *M. melitensis* organisms. Zammit and Bruce then found that 50% of the island's goats carried *M. melitensis* and that 20% of them passed the organisms into their milk. In 1904, the Malta Fever Commission traced the origin of the infection to the milk of Maltese goats. Goat milk was removed from the diet of the British troops in Malta and the incidence of undulant fever fell precipitously. Undulant fever is now called *brucellosis* in Bruce's honor.

In 1894, Bruce investigated an outbreak of nagana (trypanesomiasis of cattle) and found trypanosomes in the blood. Subsequently, the organism was called *Trypanosoma brucei.* He was the first to prove that an insect could carry protozoa of a pathologic type, and demonstrated that trypanosomes were present in most wild game animals and moreover, that they served as an intermediate host.

Tsetse flies would suck up the trypanosomes and transfer them to horses and cattle. He also showed that sleeping sickness in humans could be caused by a similar organism, *Trypanosoma gambiense*.

Bruce was accompanied on most of his trips by his wife, who was an able helper in the laboratory. He died while funeral services were being conducted for her on November 27, 1931. For his many contributions, Bruce was knighted in 1908. One of his favorite expressions was "on and on and no regrets." In 1964, Malta issued two stamps honoring Bruce and Zammit and their work. One (Scott No. 298) shows the two scientists.—Kyle, R. A., and Shampo, M. A.

PHYSICIAN
BACTERIOLOGIST

Léon C. A. Calmette (1863-1933) was born in Nice on July 12, 1863, and graduated in medicine from L'École Médécine Navale de Brest. Calmette served as a medical aid on board ship in the Far East for two years and worked with Manson in Hong Kong. He obtained his doctorate from the Faculté de Paris in 1885 with a dissertation on lymphangitis filarienne. Subsequently, he served as a physician in Gabon and Newfoundland.

Pasteur offered him the opportunity to organize a Pasteur Institute in Saigon in 1891, and while there he produced a potent therapeutic antiserum for snake bites. A flood had caused a significant increase in the cobra population. One day a snake charmer brought a box of the snakes to Calmette, knowing that he was interested in the venom. Injecting small amounts of the venom into animals, Calmette found that they became immune to lethal doses of it. And he also noted a cytolytic effect of cobra venom on mouse carcinoma.

With Roux, Yersin, and Borrell, he prepared an antipest serum during the years 1893-1894 and proved its value in a bubonic plague epidemic in 1899. He also produced large quantities of diphtheria antitoxin.

Calmette became the head of the Pasteur Institute at Lille where he studied ancylostomiasis (hookworm), a condition found in the miners of that locality. Establishing the first tuberculosis dispensary in Europe at Lille, he thereafter devoted his energies to the study of that disease. With the use of a virulent bovine strain of tubercule bacilli, and after 230 passages over a 13-year period on glycerinated potato boiled in ox bile, Calmette found that the strain was avirulent but still tuberculinogenic. The resulting product was called Bacillus-Calmette-Guérin (BCG) vaccine. Calmette injected many animals, then exposed them to virulent strains of tubercule bacilli and observed the remarkable immunity from the serum. In 1914, he vaccinated many cattle with BCG, but his work was interrupted when the Germans captured his laboratory. During his time of displacement, Calmette wrote an epic on tuberculosis with notable success.

He authorized the use of BCG to infants of tuberculous parents in 1922, and BCG vaccine was being distributed on a general basis by 1924.

In 1933, he suffered from the grippe, then infectious hepatitis, cardiac collapse, and acute peritonitis. He died on Oct. 29, 1933.

Calmette has been honored on many stamps, including a stamp issued by France (Scott No. B-232) in 1948.
—Kyle, R. A., and Shampo, M. A.

TUBERCULOSIS EXPERT A COLLEAGUE OF CALMETTE

Jean Marie Camille Guérin (1872-1961) was a great veterinary surgeon whose name is world renowned, linked with that of Calmette for their great contribution to the world in the form of the vaccine against tuberculosis, BCG (Bacillus-Calmette-Guérin).

Rarely in the history of preventive medicine has a new vaccine been the object of such probing criticism and, at the same time, enthusiastic acclaim. BCG is now known throughout the world and has helped countless thousands as a result of the interest taken in it by the World Health Organization which realized its value shortly after World War II.

M. Guérin was born in Poitiers, France, on Dec. 22, 1872. In 1892, he enrolled at L'École d'Alfort, where he began studies as a veterinary surgeon. He graduated in 1896.

Calmette and Guérin worked from 1908 to 1921 before they were satisfied with their vaccine, which they named BCG. In 1917, Calmette was named assistant director of the Pasteur Institute of Paris, and made Guérin head of the Service de la Tuberculose at Lille.

Guérin was made a member of the National Academy of Medicine in 1935, becoming president in 1950. He became a member of the Academy for Veterinarians of France in 1936. He was the vice president of the Society of Pathology and of the National Committee Against Tuberculosis. He was made laureate of the National Academy of Medicine and of the Academy of Veterinarians of France, and he received the Gold Medal of the Service of Vaccine. In 1958, Guérin received the Service Cross and the Medal of Honor in epidemiology and was an honorary member of the Ordre de Léopold (Belgium).

He died on June 9, 1961, and has been honored indirectly by a stamp (Scott No. B 232) issued by France in 1948 which shows the portrait of his co-worker, Albert Calmette.—Shampo, M. A., and Kyle, R. A.

CARRIÓN

Daniel Alcides Carrión Garcia (1857-1885), a Peruvian medical student, is among the medical martyrs and "pathfinders" who gave their lives in the cause of science. Carrión died of Oroya fever, which is known as Carrión's disease or bartonellosis after Alberto L. Barton, Peruvian physician, who later discovered the causative agent.

Carrión had permitted himself to be inoculated with material from a wart, the visible manifestation of the disease. He died 39 days later.

The disease, which also is known as *verruga peruana,* is endemic in the Andes Mountains of South America. The offending organism is a blood parasite, *Bartonella bacilliformis,* transmitted by the bite of a sand fly. Philatelically, Carrión was honored by Peru (Scott No. C149) in 1958 to commemorate the centenary of his birth.—Mirt, J. A.

NEUROLOGY
ACHIEVES
MATURITY

It has been said that Jean Martin Charcot (1825-1893) "entered neurology in its infancy and left it in its coming-of-age." Four decades devoted to medicine and France covered the interval.

Charcot was born in Paris, and received his MD degree from the University of Paris in 1853, already recognized for his scientific propensities. In 1862, he was appointed a senior physician at Salpêtrière Hospital. Ten years later, he became a professor of pathologic anatomy at the Faculty of Medicine, a position he held for a decade, lecturing at the hospital at the same time.

In 1882, he was appointed a professor of clinical neurology. The chair, the first of its kind anywhere, was created for him. He held that post until his death.

The life of Charcot and the history of Salpêtrière, an arsenal before it was converted to a hospital two centuries ago, are closely interwoven. When Charcot came to Salpêtrière, it was an asylum for the detention of women beggars, prostitutes, and criminals. Under his direction, the "pandemonium of infirmities" was transferred into a center for clinical neurologic research and teaching.

Charcot had a dominating personality. As a clinician and educator, he attracted patients and students from the world over. He was an energizing force, an investigator, and a theorist. His name is associated with amyotrophic lateral sclerosis and tabetic osteoarthropathy (Charcot's joint).

A bronze statue to Charcot, erected in the courtyard of Salpêtrière after his death (from angina) through subscriptions of his pupils, was removed by the Nazis in 1942 and melted for war purposes. However, no one has been able to eradicate the greatest memorial to him—modern neurology.

In 1960, France issued a stamp picturing Charcot and Salpêtrière (Scott No. B344), the surtax being given to the Red Cross.—Mirt, J. A.

ASTRONOMER AND PHYSICIAN

Nicholas Copernicus, (1473-1543), a Polish physician-astronomer, braved death during the Inquisition when he advanced the epoch-making theory that the sun, not the earth, was the center of the universe.

Copernicus, born Kopernik, was a native of Thorn, Prussia. His early education in Cracow included astronomy, astrology, and mathematics. He studied law in Bologna before enrolling in the Medical Faculty of the University of Padua in 1501. It is not known in what year he was graduated, but early in his medical career he served as physician for prominent families in Poland. He also had an extensive practice among the poor. His advice led to sanitary improvements which helped to combat the "black death" epidemic in Poland. He pioneered the construction of the famous aqueducts which brought water to Varmia and Pomerania.

During these busy years in medical practice and sanitation, he still found time for astronomy. His theory of the universe was published just prior to his death. Copernicus has been honored on many stamps. Poland (Scott No. 885) honored him in 1959.—Mirt, J. A.

PHYSICIAN TO
NAPOLEON BONAPARTE

Jean Nicholas Corvisart des Marets (1755-1821) was educated early to follow in the footsteps of his father, a lawyer. But the son had other ambitions—he turned to medicine, although this move meant the loss of his father's financial support.

As a consequence, his road to fame was rugged. He trained in Paris under Pierre Joseph Desault (1744-1795), one of the founders of vascular surgery, and was the youngest member of his graduation class. Corvisart practiced first as a surgeon and anatomist but later shifted to internal medicine.

In 1788, he was appointed physician to the Charité Hospital and nine years later to a professor of medicine at the Collège de France. His most famous work (1806) was *An Essay on the Organic Diseases and Lesions of the Heart and Great Vessels.* He described tetralogy of Fallot associated with right aortic arch, and his name is associated with chronic hypertrophic myocarditis. He also described the mechanics of heart failure and dyspnea of effort and a method of percussion for diagnosis of heart disorders and pathology.

When Napoleon came into power, he selected Corvisart as personal physician, named him a baron, and made him an officer of the Legion of Honor. This close contact ended with the banishment of Napoleon to Elba in 1815. The two men died but a few months apart. Corvisart was honored by a French stamp (Scott No. B385) issued in 1964, the surtax being given to the Red Cross.—Mirt, J. A.

35

BRAZILIAN
MICROBIOLOGIST

Oswaldo Cruz was a leader in public health work in Brazil, where he was instrumental in having placed the Brazilian public health service on a high and effective plane. Most of his work at the beginning of the twentieth century was as bacteriologist and parasitologist. Oswaldo Goncalves Cruz lived from 1872 to 1917, becoming director of public health in Rio de Janeiro in 1903, and ultimately the sanitary director of his nation.

Cruz was born in Saõ Luiz do Paraitinga, in Brazil, and received his MD degree from the University of Rio de Janeiro in 1892. Spurred by the discovery by Walter Reed in 1901 that yellow fever was transmitted by the bite of the mosquito, *Aëdes aegypti,* Cruz began an eradication program which turned an unhealthy city into one of the healthiest in South America.

Meanwhile Cruz had founded a research institution, renamed in 1907 the Instituto Oswaldo Cruz, for experimental pathology. There, medical scientists under his direction worked on the health problems caused by harmful insects, parasites, and venomous reptiles, with highly productive results. The organism responsible for Chagas' disease is known as *Trypanosoma cruzi.*

Brazil, in 1950, honored Cruz postally on a stamp (Scott No. 698) issued in connection with the Fifth International Congress of Microbiology.—Mirt, J. A.

THE CURIES

From a stew pot in an abandoned machine shop on the outskirts of Paris came a boon to mankind—the discovery of radium and radioactivity. As a result, the name Curie will go down in history.

Marie Sklodowska Curie (1867-1934), Polish-born chemist and physicist, studied under Pierre Curie (1859-1906) at the Sorbonne in Paris. They were married in 1896 and embarked upon a joint scientific investigation with meager facilities and a recognition of the need for infinite patience. Two years later, the world was presented with the element *radium*. In 1903, the Nobel Prize in Physics went to the Curies and to Antoine Henri Becquerel (1852-1908), discoverer of radioactivity.

The Curies pursued their investigations zealously, but tragedy struck in 1906 when the husband died as a result of a street accident. The widow succeeded him as a professor of physics at the Sorbonne and carried on relentless research in radioactivity. Her contributions in that field earned for further work on radium and its compounds the Nobel Prize in Chemistry in 1911.

The dedication to science affected her health. Constant exposure to the emanations from radium caused aplastic anemia, from which she died—another martyr to medicine. Both Madame Curie and her husband have been honored philatelically many times by many countries. The Central African Republic (Scott No. C57) honored her in 1968.—Mirt, J. A.

CHURCHMAN AND DIAGNOSTICIAN

In 1450, Nikolaus Cardinal Cusanus (1401-1464), a German Roman Catholic churchman, in his "Dialogue on Statics" suggested comparing the frequency of the pulse and respiration in disease, against that in a normal person. He believed there was a relationship and that the knowledge would help in diagnosis. But generations were to pass before these recommendations were actually put into practice. Cardinal Cusanus also suggested the weighing of blood and urine as a diagnostic aid. Germany issued a stamp (Scott No. 792) in 1958 to commemorate the 500th anniversary of the Cusanus Hospice at Kues founded by Cardinal Nikolaus.—Mirt, J. A.

DAMIEN

Joseph Damien de Veuster—Father Damien, was born January 3, 1840 in a small village in Belgium. He studied for the priesthood at the University of Louvain, later at Paris.

Although his parish was the entire island of Molokai, he arrived at the leprosy settlement, Kalaupapapa, in 1873, dying there just short of 16 years later, in 1889, of advanced leprosy, from which he had suffered for perhaps 6 to 8 years. This was confirmed by medical examination in 1885.

Father Damien, as a man of many strengths, weighed more than 200 pounds in his forties, and was vigorously active both as man and priest, "easily excited, easily peeved, and difficult to get along with at times." His fixed views and determination, carried him into all walks of life—"a good fighter," and an unyielding champion of all that lay within his work or his faith.

As a patient, Father Damien regarded his infection phlegmatically, submitting to some of the then popular but futile treatments. A photograph taken in 1887 shows him bearded, and wearing glasses, as in the Belgian stamp, (Scott No. B417) in which the artist has attempted to suggest signs of leprosy in the priest's features, and particularly in the irregularity of the earlobe.—Fite, G. L.

CHARLES DARWIN

Charles Robert Darwin (1809-1882), English naturalist and son and grandson of physicians, has had a profound effect on medicine with his theory of the origin and descent of man. Although some of his theories have been refuted, other scientists were guided along their paths which led to benefits for mankind.

Darwin was born in Shrewsbury, England. He was graduated from the University of Cambridge in 1831. Shortly thereafter, he started a five-year, around-the-world cruise on the H. M. S. *Beagle*. After his return, he labored for 20 years on his great work, *On the Origin of Species by Means of Natural Selection,* published in 1859. The book precipitated a bitter dispute between church and science in England and the United States.

In the next 22 years, Darwin produced other notable volumes on biology, psychology, and sociology. The *Descent of Man* (1871) was among these. A direct effect on medicine was his description of the tuberculum auriculae, which he insisted was evidence of a connection of man and monkey. This is known today as Darwin's tubercle.

He is buried in Westminster Abbey, and was honored in 1959 by a Polish stamp (Scott No. 880) on the 150th anniversary of his birth.—Mirt, J. A.

REVOLUTION IN
CATARACT SURGERY

Jacques Daviel (1693-1762), French ophthalmologist, in 1748 originated the modern method of treating a cataract by removing the cataracted lens through a corneal incision, without cutting the iris. In eight years, he performed 434 extractions, with only 50 failures.

This success made his technique standard practice, and it was not until a century later that any material modification was made. Then, Albrecht von Graefe (1828-1870) of Berlin added iridectomy to the operation.

Daviel was born in La Barre en-Ouche and studied medicine at Rouen and Paris. For a time he practiced in Toulon and Marseilles. During an outbreak of plague in the latter city in 1720, he was named Surgeon Major for his courage and ability, and also was given the privilege of anatomy study and surgery at the City Hospital. He eventually moved to Paris, and in 1749 was made surgeon to Louis XV. His fame spread throughout Europe and he was summoned to other courts in Europe. He died in Geneva, and France honored him philatelically (Scott No. B369) in 1963, with the surtax being given to the Red Cross.—Mirt, J. A.

MIDWIFERY

Hendrik van Deventer (1651-1724), Dutch obstetrician, has been aptly called the "Father of Modern Midwifery." His observations concerning the placental membranes and the female pelvis, and his basic studies in the anatomy of reproduction, changed the practice of obstetrics and midwifery.

Van Deventer was born at The Hague. As a youth, he became an apprentice to a goldsmith, but medicine had a greater appeal and he entered the University of Groeningen. Graduated without a formal medical degree, he took up practice in his native city. And being interested in mechanical problems, he turned to orthopedics. His wife was a midwife, and he helped her in that field by making a thorough study of the architecture and mechanics of the pelvis. He described the oblique diameters of the pelvic brim, and was the first to employ the term "placenta previa." Van Deventer was honored by a stamp issued by the Netherlands (Scott No. B175) in 1947.— Mirt, J. A.

DIAGNOSTICIAN

Josef Dietl (1804-1878) was born in Poland on Jan. 24, 1804. He studied medicine at the University of Lwow, later at Vienna, where he graduated in 1829. He became Chief of the Vienna Hospital in 1841 and a professor of medicine in 1851. A member of the school of therapeutic Nihilism, he attempted to expel the use of drugs in medicine. Although his ancestors laid much stress on the treatment of the sick, Dietl, being purely scientific, stressed the results of investigations. He thought that physicians should be judged by the extent of their knowledge and not by their number of cures. He stated that the physician who is an investigator rather than a healer should be appreciated most. Diagnosis is most important, and the patient is merely an object.

Dietl is remembered for *Dietl's crisis* which consists of kinking and obstruction of the ureter of a ptotic floating kidney, causing pain and then diuresis. It is believed to be due to a temporary hydronephrosis. Dietl became interested in politics in Krakow, where he ultimately died on Jan. 18, 1878. He was honored on a stamp (Scott No. 774) of the famous Polish physicians issued by Poland in 1957.
—Kyle, R. A., and Shampo, M. A.

BELGIUM PHYSICIAN
AND BOTANIST

Rembert Dodoens (1517-1585) was born in Malines, Belgium, on June 29, 1517. He studied medicine at the University of Louvain and graduated about 1540.

His skill at autopsy contributed much to that field, and his "Medicinolium Observationum Exampla Rara" is a collection of 54 autopsy studies. His renown led to his appointment as physician to the emperors Maximilian and Rudolph II of Austria. His greatest work, however was his Botanical Treatise on medicinal herbs, "*Cruijdboeck*," published in Antwerp in 1553.

He died in Leyden on March 10, 1585, and was honored as a physician, scientist, medical writer, and botanist on a stamp (Scott No. B323) issued by Belgium in 1942, the surtax of which went to the fight against cancer.— Shampo, M. A., and Kyle, R. A.

UNIVERSITY OF LEIDEN
OPHTHALMOLOGIST

The University of Leiden in 1840 graduated an important pioneer in medicine, Frans Cornelius Donders (1818-1889), physician and ophthalmologist. He is best known for his studies of astigmatism and of physiological optics, and is regarded as one of the founders of modern ophthalmology.

Donders started his career as an army surgeon but upon his appointment in 1848 as a professor of ophthalmology at the University of Utrecht, he devoted himself exclusively to eye diseases. Three years later, he founded in the Netherlands a hospital for the diseases of the eye.

He left traces of his labor in many facets of the vast science of physiology. The vitality of tissues, the circulation of blood, digestion, secretions, the organs of sense, and the secrets of the nervous system were fields to command his attention. He discovered the (Donder's) law of the rotation of the eyeball in 1841—the rotation of the eye around the line if sight is not voluntary (when attention is fixed upon a remote object, the amount of rotation being determined entirely by the angular distance of the object from the median plane and from the horizon). He defined and clarified many diseases of the eye. His monumental work on anomalies of refraction and accommodation (1864) gave a scientific basis to the use of glasses. His name is associated with simple glaucoma and the rainbow-like rings observed in glaucoma.

In 1863, Donders was made a professor of physiology. Three years later, he established a new physiological laboratory. He invented an ophthalmoscope, having a convex mirror with an opening in the center, which enabled a physician to examine the background of the eye. He was philatelically honored by the Netherlands (Scott No. B79) in 1935.—Mirt, J. A., Shampo, M. A., and Kyle, R. A.

DUNANT, SAINT OF
THE RED CROSS

From an elevation near Solferino, Italy, on a June day in 1859, a Swiss traveler looked down on a battle between French-Sardinian troops and Austrians. When the fighting was over 40,000 dead and wounded strewed the battlefield.

The spectator was Jean Henri Dunant (1828-1910). Seeing the lack of care for the wounded by disorganization plus the chaos among the villagers returning to their ruined homes, he took charge of the situation. For eight days, he directed the housing and care of the wounded and the burial of the dead.

Three years later, the horrors were described dramatically in *Un Souvenir de Solferino,* a book of only 95 pages, yet conveying a message that had a tremendous impact on the world. Here Dunant outlined a plan for an international organization to provide trained medical, nursing, and relief care in times of war. As a result, the International Red Cross was formed at the Geneva Convention in 1864. Over the years, almost every nation has become a signatory of the movement.

Tragedy and frustrations marked the life of this great humanitarian. He neglected his business because of his devotion to the Red Cross movement, and was thrown into bankruptcy in 1867.

Misfortunes continued to beset him, and in 1880 Dunant started 12 years of wandering through Europe. He became a forgotten man, and his health broke down. The last 18 years of his life were spent in a charity hospital in Heiden, a Swiss village.

In 1895, a newspaperman visited the village and learned about Dunant. The resulting article caused a worldwide sensation, and honors began to be paid Dunant, climaxed by the awarding in 1901 of the first Nobel Peace Prize—jointly to him and Frédéric Passy.

Philatelically, he has been honored by almost every nation in the world, a recognition no other man has ever received. More than 2,000 varieties and denominations of postage stamps bear tribute to him. Chile issued a stamp (Scott No. 322) on the centenary of the International Red Cross.—Mirt, J. A.

NEUROSURGEON

"For his discovery of the therapeutic value of leukotomy in certain psychoses" was the citation which accompanied the presentation of the Nobel Prize in Medicine and Physiology in 1949 to Antonio Caetano de Abreu Freire Egas Moniz (1874-1955), Portuguese neurologist.

It had been long known that the frontal lobes are of great importance in cerebral activity, especially in regard to the emotions, and that the destruction of the frontal lobes by bullet wound or brain tumor leads to certain changes of personality.

However, it occurred to Egas Moniz that psychic, morbid states might be relieved by destroying the connections of the frontal lobes to other parts of the brain. On the basis of this idea, he worked out an operation, the purpose of which was to interrupt these lines of communication. And since these lines of communication ran through the white matter, the operation was called prefrontal leukotomy. It was discovered that there was some response in cases of tension, fear, and anxiety, certain forms of paranoia and sometimes in schizophrenia.

Egas Moniz, born in Avanca, Portugal, studied medicine at the University of Coimbra. He became a professor there in 1902 and nine years later was appointed to the new chair of neurology at the University of Lisbon. He was a pioneer in the injection of opaque substances in x-ray visualization of blood vessel arteriography, especially of the brain. In 1931, he published a large volume on the diagnosis of cerebral tumors by this method.

His first memoirs on prefrontal leukotomy appeared in 1936. He also produced other large volumes on various aspects of medicine, including clinical neurology, sexual physiology and pathology, and medical history.

Moreover, busy as Egas Moniz was in seeking new frontiers in medicine, he took an active part in the political life of Portugal from 1903. Among important posts he held were minister to Madrid (1917), minister of foreign affairs (1917-1918), and president of the Portuguese delegation to the Peace Conference in Paris (1918).

Portugal portrayed Egas Moniz on a postage stamp (Scott No. 984) issued in 1966.—Mirt, J. A.

FATHER OF
IMMUNOLOGY

Paul Ehrlich (1854-1915) was born on March 14, 1854, in Strehlen, Silesia, Germany. He was considered an indifferent student because he was disinterested in school and dreaded examinations. While a medical student at Strasbourg, he studied the blood cells and their affinity to various aniline dyes. He developed the differential white blood count, and described mast cells, which he distinguished from plasma cells. After the discovery of the tubercule bacillus in 1882, he required only 24 hours to find a method to demonstrate its presence and acid fastness.

Ehrlich introduced quantitative methods in immunity problems, and devised methods of determining potency of toxins and antitoxins. He distinguished active immunity from passive immunity and established the meaning of these terms. And he developed the "side chain theory" —that the effect of a toxin on a particular organ was due to the cells of that organ containing receptors with a special affinity for that toxin. Toxins were fixed to the organ, whereas antitoxins were merely receptors that were produced by the body and hindered the access of toxin to living cells and thus protected the cell from injury. In his work in hemolysis, he thought that hemolysins were amboceptors and were produced by cells which acted as hemolytic factors when complexed with "fermentative complement."

Chemotherapy was a major interest of Ehrlich. He established the concept of the minimal lethal dose, a cornerstone of pharmacology. He developed trypan red for the treatment of trypanosomiasis and noted that arsenicals were trypanosidal. He developed Salvarsan "606" —a chemical used in the treatment of syphilis—this was the 606th drug he had used.

In 1908, he received, with Metchnikoff, the Nobel Prize in Medicine. He gave us the following motto: "Much work, little publication, no preliminary communications, and no guess work." This is still good advice for scientific investigators today. He died on August 19, 1915, from arteriosclerosis, diabetes, and renal insufficiency. He was honored philatelically by Germany (Scott No. 722) in 1954, which also shows a portrait of Emil von Berhring.—Kyle, R. A., and Shampo, M. A.

AUSTRIAN
NEUROSURGEON

More than a half century of devotion and contributions to neurosurgery earned for Anton von Eiselsberg (1860-1939), a professorship of surgery at the University of Vienna, and a high niche in medical annals. One historian has called him the leading surgeon of Austria.

Eiselsburg was born at Steinhaus, Austria, and was a student of Billroth. At 33, he was a professor at the University of Utrecht, The Netherlands. After three years there, he moved to Koenigsberg, Prussia, where he remained for five years. In 1901, he went to Vienna as a professor of surgery.

He produced tetany experimentally in 1892 by excision of the thyroid and parathyroids of a cat. After moving to Austria, he published many treatises on surgical problems, including brain operations, thyroid gland excisions, pituitary surgery, metastases of thyroid cancer, and transplantation. Much of his work appeared during World War I. He was killed in a train accident on Oct. 26, 1939, and was honored postally by Austria (Scott No. 653) in 1960 on the centenary of his birth.—Mirt, J. A.

BELGIAN QUEEN A PHYSICIAN

Queen Elisabeth of Belgium (1876-1965), mother of Leopold III and daughter of Duke Carl Theodor of Bavaria (who was a practicing ophthalmologist), was born on July 25, 1876. At first, she studied nursing but later changed to medicine. She received her MD degree from Leipzig in 1900. On Oct. 2, 1900, she married Prince Albert (later Albert I of Belgium).

During both World Wars, she devoted much time to the Red Cross and to the care of the wounded. Her interest in the health of her country continued thereafter, especially in the fight against tuberculosis. She left behind her a record of service which made her beloved by all Belgians. Postally, she has been honored many times by Belgium. This stamp (Scott No. 498) was issued in 1951. —Mirt, J. A.

FARABI AND
EARLY MEDICINE
IN ARABIA

Arabic medicine played a major role in Europe, Asia, and Africa in the Medieval period. This prominence arose principally through the Arabic translations of Hippocrates, Galen, and other works, rather than new contributions.

The nomadic, conquering Arabs and the Persians took a leading part in spreading Moslem civilization with its advances in sciences, philosophy, culture, and art. As their language is large and flexible, the Arabs made the products of Greek and Roman culture available throughout the world. The Arabic influence on medical writing thus created prevailed for many centuries.

Among the outstanding Islamic physicians and philosophers making use of these translations was Nasr Muhammad ibn Tarkhan ul-Farabi (870-950), generally known today as Farabi. He was born in Farab, Turkestan, and studied medicine and philosophy, which in those days were generally combined. He introduced Greek medicine and thinking to the Persians. Among those on whom he had an influence a half century after his death was Avicenna (980-1037).

The millenium of Farabi's death was marked by the issuance of commemorative postage stamps by Iran and Turkey. The latter issue (Scott Nos. 1037-40) of four denominations is a large-sized, colorful one.—Mirt, J. A.

DENTISTRY IN MEDICINE

The eighteenth century dentist, Pierre Fauchard (1678-1761), born in Brittany, France, in 1728 published his *Le Chirurgien-Dentiste,* a book which made dentistry a profession. Today, his illustrated treatise still remains as an inspiration to modern dentists.

On the cover page, Fauchard described the book as "a treatise on the teeth in which is seen the means used to keep them clean and healthy, of beautifying them, or repairing their loss, and remedies for their disease and those of the gums, and for accidents which may befall the other parts in their vicinity."

Fauchard was the first to use the orthodontal procedure in the treatment of malocclusion. He also was the inventor of many prosthetic devices. In 1746, he gave the first account of pyorrhea alveolaris, usually called Riggs Disease after the American dentist, John M. Riggs (1810-1885) who in 1870 reported a method of treatment.

Where Fauchard obtained his scientific education is not known. In 1693, he was an apprentice to the French Navy surgeon-major. Perhaps that was where he received some knowledge which subsequently was augmented by his own studies. He practiced in Nantes, Rennes, and Angers before going to Paris in 1717.

An international gathering of dentists was held in Paris in July 1961 to commemorate the 200th anniversary of Fauchard's death. French postal authorities honored the occasion with the issuance of a postage stamp (Scott No. 1003) bearing his portrait and the cover of his book.
—Mirt, J. A.

FERMI'S ATOMIC DISCOVERIES

An Italian postage stamp honors the Italian physicist, Enrico Fermi (1901-1954), who, with Arthur H. Compton and other University of Chicago scientists, split the atom and thereby gave birth to the atomic era. In the background of the stamp is the historic pile on the squash court of the University of Chicago where atomic energy was harnessed for the first time. Professor Fermi was the architect of the pile and was awarded the 1938 Nobel Prize in Physics as a result.

In the debris of a thermonuclear explosion in 1952, he discovered a new element of atomic number 100 and atomic weight 253, which was named fermium.

The world outlook was changed by the splitting of the atom. Nuclear weapons present a destructive threat. On the other hand, harnessed nuclear energy is playing a steadily increasing, constructive role in industry. Nuclear medicine is a new field of unknown potential.

Fermi was honored by Italy (Scott No. 976) in 1967 on the 25th anniversary of the first atomic chain reaction in Chicago.—Shampo, M. A., and Kyle, R. A.

ORIGINATOR OF CORNEAL TRANSPLANTATION

Every so often a major contribution is made in ophthalmology that results in the preservation or restoration of vision, or aids in the diagnosis of local or general disease. One of these was by Dr. Filatov who succeeded in devising an operative procedure for corneal transplantation that was surgically feasible.

The innovation introduced by Vladimir Petrovich Filatov (1875-1956) was the using of human eyes, taken from persons who died accidentally or after an operation. Such eyes were enucleated after death and subjected to laboratory tests. They were then placed in an air-tight receptacle and kept for one to three days in a refrigerator. This allowed ample time to obtain results of laboratory tests of the donor's tissue. The process is now developed into the "Eye Bank," which Filatov first established in 1931 and for which he was elected to the Russian Academy of Science.

Filatov was born on Feb. 15, 1875, in the town of Mikhailovka, Russia, the son of an ophthalmologist. After studying medicine at the University of Moscow, he graduated in 1897 but did not receive his medical degree until 1904. Specializing in ophthalmology, he served first at the Moscow Eye Clinic and later at the Novorossisk University in Odessa (now Odessa Medical Institute). In 1911, he became a professor of ophthalmology and Director of the Institute.

Among his contributions was the successful transplantation of skin from cadavers in the treatment of tubercular lupus vulgaris. He died in Odessa on Oct. 30, 1956, and has been philatelically honored as a great scientist and surgeon.

Russia issued a stamp (Scott No. 2659) in 1962 in his honor.—Shampo, M. A., and Kyle, R. A.

CARLOS FINLAY

Less than a century ago, yellow fever was a scourge in the United States as well as in tropical countries. As late as 1878, an epidemic broke out in the Gulf States and spread northward, taking thousands of lives.

Generally, it was believed that the disease is transmitted by clothing which comes into contact with yellow fever patients. When, in 1881, Dr. Carlos Finlay (1833-1915), a Cuban physician, advanced the theory that the disease is transmitted by the bite of a species of the "mosquito Aëdes," he was ridiculed by his medical colleagues.

It was not until after the Spanish-American War that his theory was confirmed. American troops in Cuba were dying at the rate of 200 a day. A commission headed by Dr. Walter Reed (1851-1902) was sent to the island in 1900. Reed remembered Finlay's report and decided to test the theory. Several researchers gave their lives as "guinea pigs," but medical science learned the truth. Reed reported his findings in 1901. And through subsequent years, immunization has reduced the mortality rate sharply. The disease is now under control.

Finlay, born in Camuguey, Cuba of Scottish-French parentage, received his medical degree from Jefferson Medical College, Philadelphia, in 1855. Returning to Havana, he devoted his leisure time as an ophthalmologist to a study of and experiments in tropical diseases. Soon that became his main interest. After the war, he served Cuba as Chief of the Bureau of Sanitation. Once the subject of ridicule, Finlay became a man honored the world over. Cuba honored him on an issue of 1934 (Scott Nos. 319-320).—Mirt, J. A.

PHOTOTHERAPY

Medicine is indebted to a Danish physician, Niels R. Finsen (1860-1904), for proving the therapeutic value of certain light rays. Finsen's discoveries in the field of phototherapy earned him the Nobel Prize in Medicine in 1903, shortly before his death.

Born in the Faroe Islands, he received his MD degree from the University of Reykjavik at the age of 22. Early in his medical career, he discovered the biological effect of light on animals and human beings. He applied his findings in the field of medicine.

In 1893, Finsen demonstrated the treatment of smallpox pustules by the exclusion of ultraviolet light. He produced the Finsen light from which the heat rays and most visible rays are absorbed by filters, leaving only the blue, violet, and ultraviolet rays.

Finsen carried on his research under the physical handicap of chronic heart and liver disease. Because of his contributions, he has been considered "Father of Modern Phototherapy." He was honored on the centenary of his birthday by a Danish stamp (Scott No. 377) issued in 1960.—Mirt, J. A.

ARTIFICIAL PNEUMOTHORAX FOR TUBERCULOSIS

Italy in the last half of the 19th century produced a brilliant group of surgeons and clinicians. Among these was Carlo Forlanini (1847-1918), who in 1892 developed the first artificial pneumothorax for tuberculosis therapy. With some refinements, this technique is occasionally used at the present time.

Forlanini, born in Milan, received his MD degree from the University of Pavia in 1870. He became interested in pathology, especially diseases of the lungs. He first voiced his theory of pulmonary therapy in 1882, but it was not until ten years later that he announced his successful use of the procedure. In the remainder of his life, he made numerous refinements. He was Professor of Medicine at the University of Pavia during the last 18 years of his life.

As has been the case of many physicians of note, it remained for another country to honor him postally. His portrait appears on a Belgian stamp (Scott No. B552) issued in 1953; the surtax was used for anti-tuberculosis and other charitable works.—Mirt, J. A.

FRENCH DERMATOLOGIST
AND VENEREOLOGIST

Jean Alfred Fournier (1832-1914), French dermatologist, noted that one of the symptoms of syphilis was a skin eruption. As Chief of the Venereal Disease Clinic at the St. Louis Hospital, Paris, and Professor of Dermatology at the University of Paris, he was able to carry on intensive research.

As a result, Fournier was the first to point out the syphilitic nature of ataxia and general paresis. Fournier's sign is the sharp limitation that is characteristic of a syphilitic skin lesion, as contrasted with the numerous small islets of involvement around an eczematous patch.

In 1901, he formed the Society for Moral and Sanitary Prophylaxis which carried on an educational program to control venereal diseases in France. He is regarded as a pioneer in public health. France issued a stamp in his honor (Scott No. B201), in 1946 to raise funds for the fight against venereal disease.—Mirt, J. A.

FRACASTORIUS

Girolamo Fracastoro (1483-1553), Italian physician of the Italian Renaissance known as the "Founder of Modern Epidemiology," described syphilis and gave the disease its name through the medium of poetry; he suggested the use of mercury as therapy. Prior to that, the disease had been called the "love pestilence."

Hieronymus Fracastorius, born Girolamo Fracastoro in Verona, Italy, studied at the nearby University of Padua. He entered the practice of medicine in his native city where syphilis and tuberculosis were widespread, turning his attention to those diseases.

In 1525, he published his poem, *Syphilis sive Morbus Gallicus,* with a revision five years later. His *De Contagione,* which appeared in 1546, is a more scientific discourse on that disease and tuberculosis. This book contributed greatly to the knowledge of infectious and contagious diseases and suggested the germ theory of infection. The volume also gave the first authentic account of typhus, and included a chapter on the treatment of venereal disease.

Fracastoro retired from the active practice of medicine shortly after that and devoted his time to materia medica and botany. He discovered some of the herbs used in olden times, wrote of the movements of the planets, became interested in geology, showed a concept of the refraction of light, and was the first to refer to the magnetic poles of the earth. A stroke ended his life.

Italy in 1955 issued a 25-lire stamp (Scott No. 695) with his portrait to commemorate the International Medical Congress at Verona, Sept. 1-4, 1955.—Mirt, J. A.

MEDICAL AUTHORITY FOR FOURTEEN CENTURIES

The Greek-born Claudius Galen (ca. 130-ca. 200) served as court physician for two Roman emperors, and dominated the medical thinking for 14 centuries. Open-minded in his early years, he later became one of the greatest dogmatists. It was not until Andreas Vesalius (1514-1564), Flemish anatomist, and William Harvey (1578-1657), English physiologist, provided contrary evidence, that he lost his standing as the final authority in medicine. Even today, he is remembered in the term "galenicals."

Galen was born in Pergamon, Asia Minor, seat of one of the largest temples of Asklepios. He is comparable in stature to Hippocrates (ca. 460-ca. 377 BC) in the history of Greek medicine.

Galen began the study of anatomy in his home town at 17 and added medicine and philosophy in further education at Corinth in Smyrna, and at Alexandria, Egypt. At 28, he was appointed physician to the gladiators at Pergamon. This permitted him to apply hygiene and medicine in treating the terrible wounds of contestants. Four years later, he left for Rome where he gained fame for his spectacular diagnoses and modes of treatment, physiologic demonstrations, lectures, and writing.

He served as court physician for Roman emperors Marcus Aurelius and his successor, Commodus. He made frequent journeys to other lands for study and research. When the Roman political climate became unhealthy,

Galen returned to Pergamon and presumably practiced there until his death.

The medicine and pathology of Galen were based mainly on the Hippocratic theories regarding pulse and urine, with a mixture of natural science and philosophic speculation. He was a shrewd clinician. In the fields of therapy and pharmacology, he is remembered mainly for his extremely complex descriptions and formulas. Galen also followed the teachings of Hippocrates by using diet and physiotherapy, and wrote several books on hygiene and the prevention of disease. In his youth, Galen was an able surgeon, but he gave up this branch of medicine when it came to be regarded as improper for a learned physician.

Galen's portrait appeared on a postage stamp issued in November, 1966, by the newly-formed Yemen Arab Republic (unlisted issue), to commemorate the new WHO Building in Geneva.—Mirt, J. A.

PHYSICIAN
NEUROANATOMIST

Camillo Golgi (1844-1926) was born on July 7, 1844, in Corteno, Italy, and received his MD at the University of Pavia in 1865. He later worked with Bizzozero and Lombroso who, along with Virchow's work, motivated Golgi to study the nervous system. His initial studies on the neuroglia of the gray and white matter appeared in 1870. Financial problems forced him to become a resident physician in a small town. Here, in a laboratory set up in the kitchen of his home, Golgi devised the silver chromate stain for nerve tissue.

Golgi returned to the University of Pavia, in 1875, where he spent the remainder of his academic life as a famous teacher. He later became Rector of that University. He described the Golgi type I and type II nerve cells of the cerebral cortex, as well as the musculotendinous end organs and peripheral and central nerve fibers. The cytoplasmic reticular substance of nerve and other cells has been called the Golgi apparatus since his description of it in 1889. He also made valuable contributions in the field of malaria by showing that different forms of malaria were caused by different parasites; that severity of the malaria attack depended on the number of parasites in the blood, and that the malaria paroxysm coincides with sporulation of the parasites. Golgi believed that nerve fibers within the central nervous system lost their individuality and broke up into many secondary branches which anastomosed to form a network, and he persistently refuted the neuron theory.

He described the structure of the olfactory bulb, and showed that chorea is associated with definite lesions in the nervous system. He also demonstrated the microscopic differentiation between sarcomas and gliomas of the brain.

In 1906, Golgi received the Nobel Prize in Physiology

and Medicine, jointly with Cajal. He died on Jan. 21, 1926, in Pavia at the age of 83. He was philatelically honored by Sweden (Scott No. 711) in 1966.—Kyle, R. A., and Shampo, M. A.

CUBAN MEDICAL EDUCATION

Fernando Gonzalez del Valle (1803-1899), Cuban surgeon and medical educator, was mentor for three generations. Many of his pupils at the University of Havana attained fame. In his honor, Cuba in 1958 issued a postage stamp (Scott No. 601) bearing his portrait.

Gonzalez del Valle, born in Havana, received his license to practice medicine at the youthful age of 20, a common attainment in those days. Eleven years later (1834), he was appointed the first professor of surgery at the University of Havana. When the university was reorganized in 1842, he was appointed to the Chair of Operative Medicine and External Pathology, and Head of the Surgical Clinic. His ability was recognized in Spain when he was appointed surgeon to the royal family in 1848. Subsequent recognitions were appointments as Dean of the School of Medicine (1859) and Rector of the University (1880). He was decorated with the Cross of the Order of Charles III and the Medal of the Order of Isabel the Catholic.—Mirt, J. A.

AMA PRESIDENT—
CANAL BUILDER

Health obstacles in the 1880's had defeated the French when they tried to construct a canal across the Isthmus of Panama. These problems were overcome by William Crawford Gorgas (1854-1920), an American Army surgeon who served as President of the American Medical Association in 1908-1909.

Gorgas was born in Mobile, Alabama, on Dec. 3, 1854, and was an 1879 graduate of Bellevue Medical College, New York. He became an army surgeon the following year and served as the chief sanitary officer throughout the construction of the 50½-mile canal (1904-1914), maintaining remarkable health conditions for workers not accustomed to the hazards of the tropics, especially yellow fever.

In this program, he was aided by the knowledge that the disease was caused by a small virus transmitted to man by the mosquito *Aëdes aegypti,* a fact that had been verified in 1901 by another American physician, Walter Reed. The mosquito, therefore, became the focus of attack.

In recognition of the accomplishments of Gorgas, he was made a brigadier general in 1914 and promoted to a major general 2 years later. He retired to private life in 1918 and was placed in charge of the yellow-fever survey of the International Health Board established by the Rockefeller Foundation. In 1919, he carried out a sanitary program for the Peruvian government.

Gorgas died of cerebral apoplexy in London on July 3, 1920, and was buried in the National Cemetery at Arlington, Virginia. Postally, he was honored by the issuance of a stamp from the Canal Zone (Scott No. 105) in 1928. Subsequently, he has been honored by both Panama and the Canal Zone as a great epidemiologist.—Shampo, M. A., and Kyle, R. A.

ITALIAN PHYSICIAN
AND ZOOLOGIST

Giovanni Batista Grassi (1854-1925) was born on March 27, 1854, in Rovellasca, Italy. He studied medicine at the University of Pavia, and became interested in parasitology. After graduation, Grassi quit medicine and became a zoologist and parasitologist. His initial work was with ancylostoma of the cat. He discovered the presence of worm eggs in foods and applied this finding to human ancylostomiasis (hookworm) which he verified at autopsy. He demonstrated the life cycle of *Ascaris lumbricodes* and was a penetrating reseacher into the living habits of eels, white ants, worms, and termites.

In 1883, he became professor of anatomy at the University of Catania, where he discovered the fundamental fact that no intermediary host was necessary for transmission of dwarf tape worms in humans. In 1895, he was appointed a professor of comparative anatomy at the University of Rome, and in 1898, convinced that malaria was transmitted by mosquitoes, he studied all varieties native to the Roman swamps. From his studies, he discovered, independently, the anopheles type as the true carrier of the disease, unaware of the work of Ronald Ross. However, he failed to see and identify the actual parasite carried by the insect. In 1900, he reported his work in "Studies of a Zoologist on Malaria." His work, in 1907, included the study of sandflies in which he discovered that the eggs and larvae have an important role in transmitting leishmaniasis.

He died in Rome on May 4, 1925, and has been philatelically honored as a zoologist on an Italian stamp (Scott No. 701) issued in 1955 to commemorate the 30th anniversary of his death.—Shampo, M. A., and Kyle, R. A.

PHYSICIAN AND MISSIONARY TO FISHERMEN

English physician Wilfred Thomason Grenfell (1865-1940) combined the Bible with medicine and lifted the fishermen of Labrador and Newfoundland from their morass of misery. He established health and educational facilities, turned an unproductive land into fertile fields, and made living possible in these British colonies.

Grenfell was born in Parkgate, near Cheshire, England, and received his MD degree from the London Hospital and University in 1886. After practicing for a year, he turned to missionary work among British seamen. He sailed with them in the North Sea and later with fishing fleets to Labrador and Newfoundland.

He found living conditions in the colonies appalling. The cold climate made gardening almost impossible, with the result that there was a scarcity of fresh vegetables and a prevalence of disastrous epidemics of scurvy. Trading ships, which called once or twice a year, sold merchandise at high prices and bought fish and other products for little money.

Distressed by this situation, Grenfell set up a mission in Labrador in 1891, obtained financial help, and the next year brought in a boatload of hospital supplies. He established schools, hospitals, and churches. A hospital ship, *Maraval,* was stationed at St. Anthony's, Newfoundland. In 1912, he opened a seaman's institute at St. John's.

Grenfell, in his small sailing vessel, *Strathcona II,* traveled the 1,500-mile coastline of Newfoundland and Labrador each summer. He formed a shipping line to carry fish and other products to markets and to bring back supplies for cooperative stores. Hardy and rapid-growing vegetables were introduced. Meanwhile, he continued his medical administration and missionary work.

During World War I, Grenfell was in charge of a medical unit sent overseas by Harvard University. He was knighted for his deeds. In 1934, he retired to Charlotte, Vt., where he died.

Newfoundland in 1941 issued a 5c stamp (Scott No. 252) to commemorate the 50th anniversary of his founding the Grenfell Mission.—Mirt, J. A.

PSYCHIATRIST
AND
PARASITOLOGIST

Wilhelm Griesinger (1817-1868) was born on July 29, 1817, in Stuttgart, Germany. He studied medicine at the University of Berlin and at the University of Tübingen under the guidance of Johann Lukas Schönlein (1793-1864). In 1845, he published his "Pathology and Therapy of Psychic Disorders" with which he established clinical descriptions of psychic afflictions, using ether or chloroform to treat psychoses. His efforts in the diagnosis and treatment of mental diseases earned him the name of "Father of German Psychiatry." In 1865, he succeeded Moritz Heinrich Romberg (1795-1873) as Professor of Psychiatry at the University of Berlin.

In addition, he was greatly interested in infectious diseases, and between 1857 and 1864 published his "Monographs on Infectious Diseases" in which he discussed typhus fever, typhoid fever, relapsing fever, and malaria. In 1866, he described hookworm disease as "tropical chlorosis," and established the causal relationship of *Ancylostoma duodenale* to this disease.

Eponymically, he is remembered by "Griesinger's Disease" for ancylostomiasis (hookworm) and by "Griesinger's Sign," an edematous swelling at the tip of the mastoid process in thrombosis of the sigmoid portion of the transverse lateral sinus.

He died on Oct. 26, 1868, in Berlin and was honored on a stamp (Scott No. 524) in a series issued by the German Democratic Republic (East Germany) to commemorate the 250th anniversary of the founding of the Charité Hospital in Berlin.—Shampo, M. A., and Kyle, R. A.

MEDICAL EDITOR
OF 1840

The front cover of a short-lived Cuban medical journal of the early 1840's was featured on two Cuban postage stamps (Scott Nos. 364, 365). Although the stamps were issued in commemoration of the founding of the journal, actually they were a tribute to its first editor, José Nicholás Gutiérrez y Hernández (1800-1890). He was a distinguished educator, a pioneer in delicate surgery, and an authority on cholera and other infectious diseases.

Gutiérrez was born in Havana, and received his MD degree from the university there in 1827. After his military service, he was appointed a professor of anatomy in 1830. Seven years later, he went to Europe to study continental medical practices and hospitals. After his return home, he put his knowledge to work, and at the age of 79 he became Rector of the University of Havana. The Museum of National History and the Academy of Sciences were created through his efforts.—Mirt, J. A.

महात्मा INDIA

Dr. W. M. HAFFKINE
1860 - 1930

न.पै.
15
nP

INDIA SECURITY PRESS

CHOLERA VACCINE

Waldemar Mordecai Wolff Haffkine (1860-1930) was born on March 15, 1860 in Odessa, Russia. He studied under Metchnikoff in Odessa and then went to the Pasteur Institute where he first worked as a librarian. In 1892, he reported a method of attenuation of the cholera vibrio; he had inoculated himself and a few of his friends with the attenuated organism. In 1893, he went to India where he inoculated 22,703 people during 1893 and 19,473 during 1894 in an attempt to prove the value of his vaccination. It is not known whether his cholera vaccine consisted of living or dead organisms. Most authorities thought that the vaccine was beneficial, but controversy still exists regarding its value.

He also developed a vaccine for plague, which in 1897 he tried on himself and on a few volunteers. He started a laboratory in Byculla and produced a large quantity of plague vaccine. Later, 19 of 107 patients injected with plague vaccine from a single bottle died from tetanus. This has been called the Mulkowal Disaster, and Haffkine was temporarily suspended from his work. Subsequently, a commission investigating Haffkine's work concluded that the work was not based on any new scientific principles but that it was of a great practical achievement in the area of preventive medicine. The plague research laboratory was subsequently renamed the Haffkine Institute.

Haffkine was an eccentric person; He believed himself the equal of Jenner, Pasteur, and Lister. He was very interested in religion, and thought of himself as an apostle sent for relief of suffering mankind. He died on Oct. 26, 1930, and was honored philatelically by India (Scott No. 387) in 1964.—Kyle, R. A., and Shampo, M. A.

FOUNDER OF HOMEOPATHY

Samuel Hahnemann (1755-1843) founded homeopathy, a branch of medicine employing the law of similars. He graduated in medicine at Erlangen, Germany, in 1779. And while translating Cullen's "Materia Medica" into German from English, he noticed a similarity between the effects of cinchona (Peruvian bark) on a healthy person and the results of certain diseases for which that drug was used as a cure. He concluded, after prolonged experimentation, that the cure for a disease is that drug which would, in a healthy person, produce the symptoms of such disease.

Hahnemann also advocated minimal doses of those drugs. These findings he made the basis of a school of homeopathy which he established in Leipzig. There was considerable opposition to his teachings and he left Leipzig, eventually settling in Paris. A monument to him in Washington is the most elaborate of all the medical statuary in the Capital. It cost $48,000 and was unveiled in 1900. In 1954, Brazil honored him on a stamp (Scott No. 810) issued to commemorate the First International Congress of Homeopathy.—Mirt, J. A.

MEDICAL WRITER AND TEACHER

Two and a half centuries after his birth, Albrecht von Haller's stature in medical history remains as majestic as the Alps of his homeland.

Born in Bern, Switzerland (1708-1777), Haller was a child prodigy. He studied medicine under the great teacher Herman Boerhaave, at the University of Leiden and received his MD degree at the age of 19. He went to London and Paris for further study before taking up practice in Bern. In 1736, he was appointed to the chair of medicine, anatomy, surgery, and botany at the University of Göttingen. He organized the obstetrical school, the anatomical museum, and the botanical garden, then an important facet of medical education.

One of the most prolific medical writers of all time, Haller wrote many volumes on surgery (although he never performed an operation), anatomy, physiology, and botany. He produced about 13,000 scientific papers, and the description of many anatomical structures are attributed to him. He was the first to elucidate the doctrine of the irritability of living tissue.

Haller, knighted by Empress Maria Theresa of Austria in 1749, returned to his homeland in 1753 and continued his writing. He was honored on a stamp (Scott No. B277) issued in 1958 by Switzerland.—Mirt, J. A.

HANSEN

Modern studies of leprosy began in Norway largely because of prevalence of the disease in coastal villages.

G. Armauer Hansen, at age 24 (1865), began a life's devotion to study and treatment of leprosy. He entered the field with the conviction that the cause was an infecting micro-organism, and he probably observed the bacilli as early as 1871, although not reporting the observation until 1874. His claim was confirmed by Neisser in 1879. Nothing of leprosy remains in Norway today, although tropical regions of the world still support several millions of cases, even in the face of moderately effective drug treatments.

Hansen was the author of many writings on leprosy. Two books, one on leprosy of the eye and another, published also in English, were written with the aid of coauthors. He edited the journal "Lepra" through its 13 years of existence. A modest man, he was always ready to contribute unlimited energy to his patients' welfare, as shown in a brief autobiography written late in life. The Cuban stamp (Scott No. 414), drawn from an extant photograph taken about 1900, was issued on the occasion of an International Leprosy Congress in Havana in 1948.—Fite, G. L.

DE MOTU CORDIS

William Harvey (1578-1657), English physician and physiologist, was responsible for a rebirth of the scientific spirit of modern medicine. For more than 14 centuries, the Hippocratic method of observation and experimentation had been discarded in favor of the erroneous theories of Claudius Galen (ca. 130 to ca. 200).

Galen's influence on medical practice was so strong that Harvey had difficulty in getting widespread acceptance of his scientific discovery concerning the circulation of blood. Other researchers provided confirmation after his death.

Harvey was born in Folkestone, England, and received his MD degree from the University of Padua, Italy, in 1602, followed by a second MD degree from the University of Cambridge, England. He began his practice in London, and in 1607 was made a Fellow of the College of Physicians. Two years later, he was appointed a physician at St. Bartholomew's Hospital and served in that capacity for 34 years.

Harvey was named a lecturer in anatomy and surgery at the College of Physicians in 1615. A year later, in a lecture, he first expounded his theory on blood circulation. He published a 72-page book on "An Anatomical Treatise on the Movement of the Heart and Blood" in 1628. He reported that the heart was a muscular organ with alternating contractions and expansions which sent the blood through arteries to all parts of the body, returning through veins.

In 1618, he was named "physician extraordinary" to James I and subsequently to the successor, Charles I. The appointment was ended in 1649 with the beheading of the king. Following this, Harvey retired to a quiet life. His Treatise on the "Generation of Animals," published in 1651, was the first book on embryology as we know it in modern times.

Harvey's portrait appears on postage stamps of Russia (Scott No. 1947 issued in 1957) and Argentina (Scott No. 682 issued in 1959).—Mirt, J. A.

DERMATOLOGIST CHEATS NOOSE

Grave robbing to obtain dissecting material nearly nipped in the bud the brilliant career of a Viennese dermatologist of the 19th century. Ferdinand Ritter von Hebra (1816-1880), a medical student at the University of Vienna, was found guilty and ordered to be hanged. Fortunately for dermatology, the sentence was commuted to wearing a cord around his neck for the rest of his life to remind him of his crime.

Dermatology was enriched in the middle of the 19th century by the contributions of Hebra, a member of the so-called *Second Vienna Medical School.* He deserves full credit for a classification of cutaneous disorders on the basis of structural alterations.

Hebra was born in Bruenn, Moravia, and received his medical degree from the University of Vienna in 1841. He became associated with the Allgemeines Krankenhaus and took a deep interest in cutaneous diseases. He found that scabies was a localized disease produced by the itch mite. His interest in clinical dermatology became all-absorbing, and his first treatise on classification of skin diseases appeared in 1845. His name is associated with a sulfuric ointment for pruritis as well as other therapeutic concoctions. Hebra recognized parasites and fungi as etiological agents, but omitted bacteria and other means of contagion. He gave the first description of erythema multiforme (Hebra's disease) and reported the first case of rhinoscleroma. An excellent teacher and lecturer, he attracted students from all over the world. His portrait appears on a stamp (Scott No. B160) issued by Austria in 1937.—Mirt, J. A.

SCIENTIST OF MANY TALENTS

Spectacles were invented in the 13th century; but there was no way to look into the inner recesses of the eyes until Hermann Ludwig Ferdinand von Helmholtz (1821-1894) demonstrated how it could be done.

In 1851, Helmholtz devised a crude instrument that enabled a physician to view the depths of a living human eye. The ophthalmoscope, improved by others but basically his invention, opened the doors to a new branch of medicine—ophthalmology.

Helmholtz was born in Potsdam, Germany. He received his MD degree from the Royal-Chirurgical Friedrich-Wilhelm Institute of Berlin University, with clinical instruction at the Charité Hospital.

In the next half century, he pursued investigations that embraced physics, physiology, pathology, anatomy, thermodynamics, ophthalmology, hydrodynamics, acoustics, nerve energy, color vision, and clinical medicine. Each discipline was benefited from his fertile mind.

The first of Helmholtz' scientific writings to attract general attention was an essay, *On the Conservation of Force* (1847). His *Handbook of Physiological Optics,* published in three parts between 1856 and 1867, constitute one of the great contributions to medicine in the 19th century. He described the mechanism of accommodation and the theory of color vision. He was a skilled musician and made contributions to the physiology of hearing. Eponyms linked with his name include Helmholtz's ligament of the malleus and Helmholtz's theory of sound perception.

He was appointed to the Chair of Physiology and General Pathology at the University of Königsberg, where he carried on research in physiological optics and electrical problems. In 1858, he was named a professor of physiology at the University of Bonn and three years later to a similar post at the University of Heidelberg. He returned to the University of Berlin in 1871 as a professor of physics, a post he retained until his death.

Helmholtz' portrait is on a German Democratic Republic stamp (Scott No. 62) issued in 1950.—Mirt, J. A.

CHEMISTRY AND THERAPY

The founder of the "Iatrochemical" School of medicine was Jean Baptiste van Helmont (1577-1644), Belgian physician and mystic. His work typifies the transition from alchemy to chemistry in the treatment of disease. He recognized the importance of ferments and of gas formation in physiology.

Van Helmont was born in Brussels and received his MD degree from the University of Louvain, where he later became a professor of surgery. He described carbon dioxide, studied the growth of plants, recognized the acidity of gastric juice and its importance in digestion, and described nephritis.

A devout Catholic and Capuchin Friar, he was also a natural philosopher, interweaving a fantastic supernatural concept into the interpretation of chemical investigations. He contended that a sensitive soul was the seat of the mind and the prime agent of the actions of the body.

Van Helmont had an unreasoning prejudice against human milk for a child. If milk had to be used, it should preferably be that of an ass. He also recommended panada, bread slightly sweetened with clarified honey or sugar, the whole being reduced to the consistency of a jelly, and finally diluted with sufficient beer to produce a drink. He was honored by a Belgian stamp (Scott No. B 322) issued in 1942.—Mirt, J. A.

FATHER OF MEDICINE

"I swear by Apollo, the physician, by Aescularius . . ." goes the traditional oath of a new physician. Not all medical schools administer the oath of Hippocrates; some have returned to the Creed of Maimonides, which prays for strength.

Scientific advancement in European medicine centers in Hippocrates (460-377B.C.). He gave to Greek medicine its scientific spirit and its ethical ideals.

Born on the island of Cos, he received his first medical instruction from his father. Further experience was gained by extensive travel. He introduced the art of clinical inspection and observation. He knew the use of many drugs but usually confined his treatment to plain expediencies, such as fresh air, diet, purgatives, blood-letting, and massage. Naturally, most of his theories have been abandoned as medicine became more scientific.

Hippocrates was a capable writer, giving the world the first script on medical history. Tradition has it that he did his teaching under a plane tree on the island, a tree supposedly in existence to this day. He has been honored by many issues of Greece, and is shown on a 1966 issue of the Yeman Arab Republic (unlisted issue) which depicts the new WHO building in Geneva.—Mirt, J. A.

THE "NEW VIENNA SCHOOL"

Joseph Hyrtl (1810-1894), born in Hungary, was the first and greatest teacher of topographic and regional anatomy in the 19th century. One of the founders of the new Vienna school of medicine, his interest in comparative anatomy marked the beginning of methodical research in that field.

Hyrtl was graduated from the University of Vienna in 1835. Two years later, he became a professor of anatomy at the University of Prague. He assumed a similar position at the University of Vienna in 1844, remaining there for 30 years.

A splendid instructor and orator, he was admired by his pupils who came from far and near. He improved anatomical techniques, and under his leadership anatomy took on new importance throughout Europe. Through his influence, an excellent anatomical museum was established. He described an anastomotic loop between the right and left hypoglossal nerves in the genicohyoid, as well as an incomplete band of circular muscle fibers in the rectum, four inches above the anus.

After his retirement from the University of Vienna, he devoted 20 years to writing, contributing much valuable material to medical literature. Having known the bitterness of poverty in his youth, he left his large fortune to charitable organizations. He was honored postally by Austria (Scott No. B162) in 1937 in the Famous Austrian Physicians series.—Mirt, J. A.

HIGH PRIEST OF
ANCIENT MEDICINE

Im-Hotep, who lived in the ancient Egyptian city of Memphis about 2900 B.C., was vizier (high priest) and physician to King Zoser of the third dynasty (2980-2900 BC). Im-Hotep, meaning "he that cometh in peace," was to the Egyptians what Asklepios was to the Greeks.

Magic played an important part in medicine in those days. Magician-physicians were trained in the Memphis Temple, where Im-Hotep worshipped and which was used as a hospital-medical school. After his death, he was looked upon as a demigod. Later (about 500 BC), he was deified as a god of medicine.

In 1928, the Egyptian postoffice department issued two stamps to honor the 1st International Congress of Tropical Medicine held in Cairo. One stamp (Scott No. 153) shows Im-Hotep upon a throne; in his right hand he is holding a scepter, a symbol of power; his left holds the "ankh," symbol of life.—Mirt, J. A.

91

VACCINATION
BEFORE 1800

Jan Ingenhousz (1730-1799), a Dutch-born physician, reported in 1779 the process by which plants convert carbon dioxide and water into simple carbohydrates. Based on this knowledge, other scientists have made advancements in chemistry as well as agriculture.

Ingenhousz, born in Breda, Holland, received his MD degree from the University of Louvain in 1752. He practiced in Holland and England. In 1778, he was called to the Austrian court by Empress Maria Theresa to inoculate three members of her family against smallpox after two other members had died from the disease. This was done after preliminary experiments upon 200 Viennese children. Upon his return to England, he was elected a Fellow of the Royal Society. He died in Bowood, England. He was honored on a stamp (Scott No. B135) issued by the Netherlands in 1941; the surtax was given for cultural and social relief.—Mirt, J. A.

PIONEER IN VIRUS DISEASE

Dmitry Iositovich Ivanovsky (1864-1920) was a Russian microbiologist who did pioneer work in the study of viruses. Through research conducted with tobacco plants infected with disease, he was the first to demonstrate that viruses could pass through a filter which would remove bacteria, and he was the first to observe the presence of intracellular bodies in diseased plants. He believed that these intracellular bodies were the result of the disease. In his studies of the structure of diseased plants, he also described the existence of crystalline bodies and crystals. As a professor at St. Petersburg University and later at Moscow University, and because of his contributions to the study of viruses, he was honored as a great scientist by the issuance of a Russian stamp (Scott No. 2938) on the centenary of his birth.—Kyle, R. A., and Shampo, M. A.

MASS
MEDICINE

     Mass chemotherapy carried out under the direction of Eugene Jamot (1879-1937), French physician, reduced substantially the mortality and morbidity from sleeping sickness in the French African colonies.

     A study which he made in 1929 with the aid of 30 physicians and sanitary officials and 300 natives included 640,652 natives and showed 112,796 persons (17.6%) affected. In some areas more than half of the population carried the culprit trypanosome. This organism is a species of the flagellate which is transmitted through the bite of the blood-sucking tsetse fly. Jamot was accorded the highest honors of the French Academy of Science. Postally, he was honored in 1954 by Cameroun (Scott No. C33) on the 75th anniversary of his birth.—Mirt, J. A.

BEGINNINGS OF MEDICAL WELFARE

A bank clerk who turned to medicine became New Zealand's most renowned promoter of child welfare. Frederick Truby King (1858-1938) received his medical degree from the University of Edinburgh in 1880 and his BSc six years later after studying public health. He returned to New Zealand where child welfare became his principal interest.

In 1907, with the financial aid of Lady Plunkett, wife of the governor of New Zealand, he established the Plunkett System. The organization trained nurses in child care and eventually became world-wide in scope.

King, an honorary member of the American Pediatric Society, was knighted in 1925. He is shown on a stamp (Scott No. 318) issued by New Zealand in 1957 to commemorate the 50th birthday of the Plunkett Society. —Mirt, J. A.

ROBERT KOCH — MICROBIOLOGIST

Koch (1843-1910) started his medical career in 1866 as a German village "horse and buggy doctor." Later, he was to become a world-renowned researcher in bacteriology, and was awarded the 1905 Nobel Prize in Medicine and Physiology for his discoveries of the causes of tuberculosis and cholera.

Koch was born in Klausenthal, Prussia. One of 13 children in a family of poor circumstances, he was on the road to becoming a shoemaker. A burning desire for biological knowledge induced his parents to make sacrifices and send him to the University of Göttingen, South Prussia, where he received his MD degree in 1866.

With a microscope given to him by his wife on his 28th birthday, he set up a laboratory in his home. Patients were scarce, so he spent many hours in his laboratory. Anthrax was devastating cattle and sheep in Europe, and he worked tirelessly on that problem. In 1876, he announced the discovery of the anthrax bacillus.

When Koch was appointed to the Imperial Health Office in Berlin in 1880, he turned his entire attention to bacteriology. Two years later, at a meeting of the Philosophical Society, he announced the discovery of the tubercle bacillus. In 1890, he introduced tuberculin as a cure, provoking world-wide excitement before the serum was discovered to be harmful. Some good resulted from this, however. It led to the Koch phenomenon, a localized inflammatory reaction which indicated previous exposure to the tubercle bacillus (tuberculin test). Effective management of tuberculosis was not achieved until soil and organic chemists produced antibiotic drugs more than 60 years after Koch's discovery of the causative agent.

In 1883, Koch was sent by the German government to Egypt and India to find the cause of Asiatic cholera. He discovered the *Vibrio comma* was the responsible organism. In 1885, he was appointed a professor in the department of hygiene of the University of Berlin. Six years later, he was named head of the newly created Institute of Infectious Diseases (afterward renamed the Koch Institute).

Koch spent the last 15 years of his life delving into many problems of medicine, including bubonic plague in India, cattle plague in South Africa, tsetse fly-sleeping sickness disease in west Africa, and malaria in the East Indies. He received many medical honors. On a visit to New York in 1908, he was made an honorary member of the Academy of Medicine.

Postally, Koch has been honored often. His portrait appears on postage stamps of West Germany, German Democratic Republic, Belgium, Danzig, Romania, Russia, and Sweden. His portrait is shown here on a stamp (Scott No. B251) issued by Germany in 1944 to commemorate the centenary of his birth.—Mirt, J. A.

THYROIDECTOMY PIONEER

Goiter was endemic in the Swiss Alps at the turn of the 20th century. This provided Emil Theodor Kocher (1841-1917) with clinical material for more than 5,000 thyroidectomies over a 45-year period. In return, he gave medicine an understanding of the physiology and pathology of the thyroid gland in toxic and nontoxic goiter.

Kocher developed an operative technique that cut the mortality from 12.8% in his first series of cases to one death in a series of 600 cases. For his contribution to medicine he was awarded the 1909 Nobel Prize.

The name of Kocher is associated with other operations, including excision of the ankle joint, resection of the wrists, repair of inguinal hernia, excision of the tongue in carcinoma, hypophysectomy, gastroduodenostomy, and a procedure for a reduction of dislocation of the shoulder joint. He also was the first to describe the abdominal reflex following pressure of the testicles. His textbook *Operative Surgery* (1894) was standard for a generation.

Kocher was born in Bern, Switzerland in 1841, and received his MD degree from the University of Bern in 1865. He studied further in Berlin, London, Paris, and Vienna. In 1872, he was appointed a professor of clinical surgery in the University of Bern and head of the University Surgical Clinic.

Colloid goiter was a common finding in the clinic and the gravitation of Kocher to that field was natural. He was diligent and original in his research and effective in teaching as well as an expert in operating.

Kocher invented numerous instruments, including Kocher's forceps in general use today. For many years, his clinic was a mecca for visiting surgeons from all parts of the world.

The Swiss Postal Administration in 1967 marked the 50th anniversary of his death with a postage stamp (Scott No. B365) bearing his portrait.—Mirt, J. A.

DUTCH PHYSICIAN PROMOTES
PSYCHIATRIC CARE

J. C. Schroeder van der Kolke (1797-1862), born in the Netherlands, studied medicine at the University of Groningen and graduated at the age of 20. He became a professor of anatomy and physiology at the University of Utrecht, where he introduced microscopic and experimental techniques in the study of histology.

His most important efforts were in the field of mental health. He introduced better nursing and medical care in insane asylums and was instrumental in the passage of the Lunacy Act of 1841. He became an inspector of lunatic asylums and exerted great influence on the government and asylum directors. He died in Utrecht on May 1, 1862, and was honored philatelically by The Netherlands (Scott No. 383) in 1960.—Kyle, R. A., and Shampo, M. A.

SURGEON CONTROLS
SLEEPING SICKNESS

Tropical diseases were the chief interest of Lisbon-born Aires José Kopke (1866-1947). He entered the Portuguese Navy's tropical disease service after receiving his MD degree from the University of Lisbon Medical School in 1889.

Gambian trypanosomiasis, also called mid-African sleeping sickness, was a serious health and economic problem in the Portuguese mid-African colonies. Kopke was assigned to the task of controlling the disease. He used sodium arsenate (atoxyl) with success.

As a result, Kopke received widespread recognition as an epidemiologist. He was elected a member of the Portuguese Society of Biology and the Lisbon Society of Medical Sciences. His foreign honors included election to membership in the Royal Institute of Public Health and Hygiene, the Royal Society of Tropical Medicine and Hygiene, London, and the Society of Tropical Pathology, Paris.

Kopke is pictured on a 1967 postage stamp (Scott No. 394) of St. Thomas and Prince Islands, Portuguese possessions off the west coast of Africa. Also shown are a microscope; *T. gambiense,* the cause of the disease; and the tsetse fly *(Glossina palpalis),* which transmits the trypanosomes of sleeping sickness in man.—Mirt, J. A.

STRUGGLE AGAINST TUBERCULOSIS

Baron Frigyes von Tolcsva Koranyi (1828-1913) was born Fredrich Kronfeld in Hungary on Dec. 20, 1828. He studied medicine at the University of Budapest, from which he graduated in 1851, and at which university he became a professor of internal medicine. Later, he served as Rector of the University. His name is associated with physical diagnosis of tuberculosis and pleural effusion. In 1908, he was made a baron.

He was one of the first champions and leaders against tuberculosis in Hungary, and his work resulted in the building of four large institutes and a network of dispensaries devoted to control and treatment thereof. He died in Budapest on May 13, 1913, and was honored philatelically by Hungary (Scott No. 1103) in 1954.—Kyle, R. A., and Shampo, M. A.

LAËNNEC

The stethoscope is a basic identification of the physician, because it is one of his most important tools. Sounds transmitted by it disclose abnormal conditions of the heart and lungs.

René Théophile Hyacinthe Laënnec (1781-1826), French physician, was once faced with a patient who refused to permit him to place his ear on her chest. Having observed children at play transmit sound through a wooden beam by tapping one end and listening to the other, he constructed a foot-long tube. Through this he could hear the heart sounds of his patients more clearly.

Laënnec then constructed a durable and satisfactory wooden stethoscope. In 1819, he published a treatise on auscultation with detailed information on all the cardiac and pulmonary sounds he had heard.

Born in Quimper, Brittany, Laënnec received his preliminary training from an uncle, a professor of medicine at the University of Nantes. This was followed by three years at the École de Médécine in Paris. At his graduation, in 1804, he received the Grand Prix in medicine and surgery.

Laënnec was chief editor of the *Journal de Médecine*. He wrote prolifically on pathological anatomy, describing diseases of the chest, peritonitis, cirrhosis of the liver, and other morbid conditions. His name is associated (Laënnec pearls) with soft casts of the smaller respiratory passages expectorated in bronchial asthma. Clinical observations were correlated with postmortem findings. During this period, he also held posts at the Hospital Beaujou and at the Salpêtrière. But his fame rests upon his stethoscope, found in the pocket of every physician today.

Laënnec was appointed to the Chair of Medicine at the College de France at the age of 41. In the following year, he succeeded his teacher, Corvisart, as full professor of medicine. His death, three years later, was caused by pulmonary tuberculosis.

Laënnec's short life was full of accomplishments despite handicaps. He appears on a French postage stamp (Scott No. 685) issued in 1952.—Mirt, J. A., Shampo, M. A. and Kyle, R. A.

PRE-VESALIAN ANATOMY

Spain in the 16th century produced many anatomists of renown. Among them was Andrés Laguña (ca. 1494-1560). He published a compendium on dissection in 1535, nearly a decade before the appearance of Vesalius's *De Humani Corporis Fabrica.*

Where Laguña received his medical education is open to debate. One report is that he received his MD degree from the University of Toledo, and another that he was first educated at Salamanca, once the center of Arab learning in Europe, and later at Padua and Bologna. He was regarded as a physician of skill and served Popes Paul III and Julius III (Emperor Charles V).

Laguña in 1542 described the ileocecal valve and the next year a method of excising vesicourethral caruncles of the bladder. His later contributions to medical literature included a treatise on diseases of the joints, the life of Galen, and a dietary system for the poor.

A portrait of Laguña is shown on a stamp (Scott No. 1464) of the "Famous Spanish Physicians" set issued in 1967.—Mirt, J. A.

DISCOVERY OF
BLOOD GROUPS

In Karl Landsteiner (1868-1943) "Father of Blood Grouping," it would be hard to find a physician whose life better exemplified the ideals of the scientific worker. Landsteiner, born of Jewish parents in Vienna, June 14, 1868, graduated as an MD from the University of Vienna at 23. He was successively a research chemist for five years in the famous laboratories of Emil Fischer, E. Bamburger and Hantsch, an assistant at the Hygiene Institute of Vienna to Prof. Max von Gruber, an assistant at the Pathological Anatomical Institute of the University of Vienna, pathologist at the R. K. Ziekenhuis in The Hague, and finally at the Rockefeller Institute in New York. He continued his investigations on immunity and individual blood differences for many years.

Landsteiner received the Nobel Prize in Medicine in 1930 in recognition of his discovery of blood groups in man through research done in 1900. He introduced dark-field microscopy for the diagnosis of primary syphilis. With his co-worker, Donath, he elucidated the mechanism of causation of paroxysmal cold hemoglobinuria, and with co-worker Clara Nigg succeeded in cultivating rickettsia in tissue cultures. He demonstrated the specificity of antigens responsible for protection of an individual against a second attack of the same viral disease. This specificity of chemical structure founded the science of immunochemistry.

Landsteiner believed that the blood of an individual was as unique a characteristic as fingerprints. With Dr. Philip Levine, he discovered the M and N blood groups useful in forensic medicine in cases of disputed paternity. His research with Wiener led to the eventual discovery of the Rhesus (Rh) factor.

He has been honored philatelically by two countries, Austria (Scott No. 813) and East Germany, (Scott No. 1025) on the 100th anniversary of his birth.—Matejka, J. J.

BARON LARREY —
MILITARY SURGEON

Dominique Jean Larrey (1766-1842), French surgeon, is regarded as the founder of military medicine. He instituted the practice of immediate surgical care of the wounded on the battlefield and then their quick evacuation to the rear by means of so-called "flying ambulances."

Larrey, orphaned at 13, was reared and educated by his uncle, Alexis, director of the Surgical College in Toulouse. This was followed by study of surgery in Paris. At 21, he was appointed as an assistant naval surgeon on a vessel bound for Newfoundland.

Larrey returned to the continent in the midst of the French Revolution in 1789. He resigned his naval commission and continued his study of medicine at the Hôtel Royal des Invalides and L'Hôtel Dieu in Paris.

At the outbreak of war with Austria and Prussia in 1792, he was attached to the French Army of the Rhine. A capable and fearless surgeon, Larrey performed as many as 200 amputations in 24 hours. It was in this campaign that he developed the "flying ambulances."

Shortly after the turn of the 19th century, Napoleon found himself embroiled in a war against most of Europe, and Larrey served as Chief Surgeon in Napoleon's Army. He was wounded on three occasions, and the last time, at Waterloo, was left for dead. When he regained consciousness, he made an unsuccessful attempt to escape. Sentenced to death, Larrey was reprieved and given safe conduct to a neutral country. In later years, he again taught surgery in Paris. His name is associated with a surgical procedure for amputation of the arm, a special bandage, and ligation of the femoral artery just below Poupart's ligament. He spent his last six years in retirement.

Larrey's evacuation concepts were ignored by other nations until the United States was well into the Civil War. Then his surgical ideas were adopted at the Battle of Antietam.

Larrey, in military uniform, is pictured on a French postage stamp (Scott No. B386) issued in 1964, the surtax being given to the Red Cross.—Mirt, J. A.

FRENCH PHYSICIAN DISCOVERS MALARIA PARASITE

Charles Louis Alphonse Laveran (1845-1922) was born on June 18, 1845, and graduated in medicine from the University of Strasbourg in 1867. He later became an army surgeon and served in Algeria from 1878 to 1883.

Laveran studied the pigment of the liver and brain in patients who had died from malaria and demonstrated that certain of the pigment granules showed amoeboid movement in the blood. Finding that these bodies were crescentic or spherical, he thought that they were parasites. He became convinced when he found flagellation of the male crescent, thus proving the malarial parasite, in 1880. He shared the view with A. F. A. King that human malaria was mosquito borne, but he was unable to test this theory, nor did he recognize the three major types of malaria. But he continued to write about malaria and forwarded the cause of tropical medicine and hygiene throughout the French colonial possessions.

Laveran joined the Pasteur Institute in 1897, and seven years later wrote a book with F. Mesnil on trypanosomes and trypanosomiasis. He did experimental work and tested many remedies for therapy of sleeping sickness. In 1917, he wrote a large treatise on leishmaniasis.

In 1907, Laveran received the Nobel Prize in Medicine. New fields in parasitology and tropical medicine were opened through his research studies. And he was honored philatelically by Algeria (Scott No. 252) in 1954.
—Kyle, R. A., and Shampo, M. A.

INVENTOR OF
THE MICROSCOPE

A Dutch janitor and draper, Antonj van Leeuwenhoek (1632-1723), of Delft, had little knowledge of medicine and only a minimal exposure to formal education. Yet his discoveries and inventions had a profound influence upon medicine, not only in his lifetime, but even more so a century or two later.

His inquisitive nature concerning the minute world of protozoa and bacteria, plus his mechanical skill, led to the construction of microscopes of such power that they revealed living creatures previously invisible to man. Through his invention, he was able to describe a great number of animate and inanimate objects. He discovered spermatozoa as a regular constituent of semen, contributing to an understanding of human fertilization and reproduction. A new science, microbiology, began.

He also discovered the red blood corpuscles, the striated character of voluntary muscles, the structure of the lens of the eye, and various microorganisms. He reported his findings in a steady stream of halting, ungrammatical letters to the English Royal Society, which eventually honored him by electing him a Fellow in 1680.

Showing no interest in medicine, Leeuwenhoek made no effort to correlate bacteria with contagion and disease. It was not until a century later that bacteriologists discovered this relationship and began to develop preventive measures. He has been honored on a stamp (Scott No. B97) issued by the Netherlands in 1937.—Mirt, J. A.

SCOTTISH CONTRIBUTOR TO TROPICAL MEDICINE

William Boog Leishman (1865-1926) was born in Glasgow, Scotland, on Nov. 6, 1865, and was graduated from Glasgow University with an MD degree in 1886. The following year he joined the British Medical Service and was sent to India.

He returned to Europe 10 years later and became associated with the Army Medical School in Netley and Millbank, England. During this period, he developed a modification of Romanowsky's stain for the identification of agents of tropical diseases. He discovered the Leishman-Donovan bodies in mononuclear phagocytes, which are pathognomonic for kalazar (dumdum fever). He also studied phagocytosis of leukocytes, which led to the concepts of opsonins and the opsonic index.

Leishman did extensive work on the dose, interval, and mode of administration of typhoid vaccine, and subsequently organized the typhoid vaccine program for the British Expeditionary Forces in World War I.

Knighted in 1909 and elected a Fellow of the Royal Society the following year, Leishman was an original member of the Medical Research Committee (later Medical Research Council). He became Director-General of the Army Medical Service and also served on the Yellow Fever Commission in West Africa.

He died in London on June 2, 1926, and was honored postally on a stamp of Brazil (Scott No. 938) issued in 1962. The stamp pictures Dr. Gaspar Vianna and commemorates the 50th anniversary of the discovery of the treatment (by intravenous injection of potassium antimony tartrate) of leishmaniasis.—Kyle, R. A., and Shampo, M. A.

BRAZILIAN MEDICAL MARTYR

Oliveira Gaspar Vianna (1885-1914), Brazilian pathologist, lived only 29 years but in that short span of life he made a valuable contribution to tropical medicine. Two years before his death, he reported the successful use of antimony tartrate as an antiprotozoan agent in the treatment of leishmaniasis.

Gaspar Vianna, who was born in Brazil, received his MD degree from the University of Rio de Janeiro. He served as an assistant in the Institute of Oswaldo Cruz in Brazil. It was there that he developed his interest in tropical diseases. He continued in that field as a professor in the Brazilian College of Agriculture. His death was due to sepsis contacted at autopsy. He was honored philatelically (Scott No. 938) by Brazil in 1962 on the 50th anniversary of his treatment for leishmaniasis.—Mirt, J. A.

MEDICAL EDITOR, TEACHER, HISTORIAN

Maximiano Augusto de Oliveira Lemos, Jr. (1860-1923), a great contributor to military and legal medicine, attended the Medical and Surgical School of Oporto, Portugal. Following his graduation, Lemos became a military medical officer. In 1880, he was appointed assistant professor at the Oporto Medical School—the beginning of a brilliant, 42-year teaching career. He taught legal medicine, general pathology, and general medical practice. He was Director of the Faculty of Medicine and Vice-Rector of the university when carcinoma forced his retirement shortly before his death at 63. The Lemos Institute of Hygiene at Lisbon is a memorial to him. Lemos was deeply interested in medical history and served as an editor of the Archives of Medical History of Portugal.

Maximiano de Oliveira Lemos is pictured on a Portuguese stamp (Scott No. 989) issued in 1966.—Mirt, J. A.

LEONARDO

"The Last Supper" and "Mona Lisa" of Leonardo da Vinci (1452-1519) are the highlights of his brilliant and varied career. But medicine owes him a debt of gratitude, too, because he laid the groundwork for the technique and profession of medical illustration.

Leonardo studied the human body closely and portrayed it in minute detail. He produced anatomical drawings, wrote voluminous notes on physiology, and commented on diseases, most of which was sound scientifically. These commentaries were based largely on studies of dissected cadavers and animals.

Da Vinci's postmortem activities came to an end in 1516 when Pope Leo X placed a ban on dissections. On the invitation of Francis I of France, Leonardo then took up residency in a castle near Ambroise, where he lived out the remainder of his life.

Leonardo, born in the Tuscan village of Vinci, was self-educated in physiology and anatomy. He apparently was familiar with Galenic anatomy but he approached medicine more scientifically. He has been credited with knowledge of arteriosclerosis. The eye, muscles of the tongue, heart valves, position of the fetus in the womb, and the bladder are among other anatomical phases covered in his writings.

Many postage stamps have honored him. Trieste (Zone A) honored him with a stamp (Scott No. 145) issued on the 500th anniversary of his birth.—Mirt, J. A.

SURGERY OF
BLOOD VESSELS

René Leriche (1879-1955), who received his MD degree from the University of Lyon, France, in 1903, was a leader in neurological and vascular surgery. He made important contributions toward an understanding of nerve blocks and of the treatment of vascular accidents by the infiltration of the stellate ganglion.

In 1917, he initiated Leriche's operation for the relief of vascular disturbances. He also originated arteriectomy and surgery of the sympathetic nervous system. His development of ganglionic blockage by procaine made surgery less painful, especially in childbirth. The eponym, "Leriche's syndrome," refers to aorto-iliac occlusive disease and intermittent claudication of the lower extremities, with pain in the hips and buttocks.

Leriche, in 1924, was made a professor of clinical surgery at the University of Strasbourg. He was elected to the Collège de France in 1938, and appeared as a guest professor or speaker before universities and medical organizations in the United States as well as in Europe. Among the institutions conferring honors on him were Harvard University and Western Reserve University.

Leriche was born in Roane, Loire, France. His portrait appears on a 35-franc postage stamp (Scott No. 868) issued by France in 1958.—Mirt, J. A.

CONTRIBUTOR TO
THE DEVELOPMENT
OF MICROBIOLOGY

Constantin Levaditi (1874-1953) was born in Galatz, Romania, in 1874. After graduating from medical school in Bucharest, he worked with Victor Babes and then moved to the Ehrlich Institute in Frankfort. He joined the Pasteur Institute in 1900 where he worked with Metchnikoff and Roux. Two years later, he authored books on the mast cell and granules in leukocytes. He became interested in syphilis and was the first (1905) to demonstrate the presence of *Treponema pallidum* in a newborn with congenital lues. In collaboration with Pierre Marie, he showed that the antigen in the Wasserman reaction was nonspecific, later showing that this antigen was a hepatic lipid. He is best known for his method of staining *T. pallidum,* the agent of syphilis, with silver. He subsequently pioneered syphilis therapy with bismuth and arsenical compounds.

With Karl Landsteiner, he observed in 1910 that poliomyelitis was due to a filterable virus. Levaditi also contributed to the knowledge of the viruses of epidemic encephalitis, herpes, rabies, and coxsackie. In later years, he wrote on the therapeutic application of streptomycin and chloramphenicol. He died on Sept. 5, 1953, and has been honored by Romania (Scott No. 1499) in 1962.— Kyle, R. A., and Shampo, M. A.

CHEMISTRY IN MEDICINE

One of the best examples of medicine's debt to chemistry is to the compendium of contributions by Justus von Liebig (1803-1873).

Liebig received his PhD degree from the University of Erlangen after earlier study at the University of Bonn. He then studied briefly in Paris. His appointment as Professor Extraordinary of Chemistry at the University of Giessen, at the age of 21, gave him an opportunity to expand his chemical investigations and to establish an educational laboratory.

He was a pioneer investigator of metabolism, discoverer of chloral hydrate and hippuric acid, and was among the first to prepare chloroform. Other new and important contributions to chemistry followed in rapid succession. His achievements brought him knighthood in 1843. He has been honored on a stamp (Scott No. 695) issued by Germany in 1953, the 150th anniversary of his birth.—Mirt, J. A.

ANTISEPSIS AND SURGERY

Joseph Lister (1827-1912) was born on April 5, 1827, at Upton, Essex, England. His father, a wine merchant, had a hobby—microscopy, which gained for him a fellowship in the Royal Society. Lister obtained his bachelor of medicine degree from London's University College and went to the University of Edinburgh where he studied under James Syme. He prospered and became a well-known surgeon. Lister invented a needle for silver wire used as suture material, a hook for removing foreign bodies from the ear, blunt scissors for cutting bandages, a tourniquet for compressing the abdominal aorta, and sterile catgut sutures.

He was concerned about infection following surgical procedures and, after studying Pasteur's work, believed that germs were the cause of putrefaction in wounds. He was the first to advocate cleanliness and the use of soap and water. He then employed carbolic acid in treating a compound fracture in an 11-year-old boy in 1865. He treated 11 other patients for compound fractures within the next two years, and in only one of these was amputation necessary. Previously, amputation had been the usual procedure for compound fractures because of complicating infections. And Lister used other antiseptics, including bichloride of mercury and boric acid.

Ultimately, Lister headed the Department of Surgery at Kings College Hospital in London and, after considerable efforts, won over his colleagues in London to antiseptic techniques.

He died on Feb. 10, 1912, and was honored philatelically (Scott No. 427) by Great Britain in 1965.—Kyle, R. A., Shampo, M. A., and Mirt, J. A.

TRAGEDY MARKS DISCOVERY OF ANESTHESIA

Failure to publicize the fact that ether had been used as a general anesthetic almost cost Crawford W. Long (1815-1878) the honor of being the first to use ether for that purpose. After some years with considerable controversy, it is now an accepted fact that the honor goes to him. He used the drug for the removal of a tumor on the neck of a patient in 1842—James Venable. And the fee was $2.00 for the operation and 25c for the ether!

Long received his MD degree from the University of Pennsylvania in 1839 and returned to his native state of Georgia to practice. His discovery of ether three years later was not recorded in medical annals until others had reported similar experiences in tooth extraction in October, 1846. Long's first article on the subject was published in December, 1849.

Tragedy marked the discovery of this great boon to mankind. Long died in obscurity. Three others (Wells, Morton, and Jackson) identified with the early use of ether in dentistry were involved in litigation. One became insane and committed suicide, another went insane, and the third died in poverty. Long's portrait is on a stamp (Scott No. 875) issued by the United States in 1940.— Mirt, J. A.

BACTERIOLOGY IN BRAZIL

Adolfo Lutz (1855-1940), Brazilian bacteriologist, entomologist, and zoologist, devoted more than three decades to medicine. His principal interest was tropical diseases, and in that field he contributed many original and corroborative investigative studies. Lutz described the first case of South American blastomycosis in 1908.

Lutz, born in Brazil, received his MD degree in 1877. After postgraduate education in Austria, Germany, and France, he returned to his native country. There, as director of the Saõ Paulo Bacteriological Institute (1893 to 1908), he succeeded in reducing the mortality from cholera and yellow fever in Brazil. He was honored in a stamp (Scott No. 830) issued by Brazil in 1955 on the centenary of his birth.—Mirt, J. A.

MALARIA FIGHTER

François Clemente Maillot (1804-1894), a French army surgeon, served as a health officer in Algeria. In the middle of the 19th century, he directed an aggressive campaign against malaria with the use of quinine. The disease was of epidemic proportions before he entered the field.

Maillot was born in Briey, Moselle, France, and received his MD degree from the University of Paris in 1828. He entered the army, which sent him to French Africa as a health officer. His last assignment was as physician-in-chief at a hospital in Bone, Algeria, a seaport town. In 1878, he retired at the age of 74, returning to France, where he died 16 years later.

An Algerian postage stamp (Scott No. 251) issued in 1954 bears his portrait and the inscription "Traîtement du Paludisme," the field in which he played an important role.—Mirt, J. A.

רבי משה בן מימון

MAIMONIDES

דתתצ"ה - תתקס"ה
1135 - 1204

JEWISH PHYSICIAN AND PHILOSOPHER

Faced with the ultimatum of embracing the Islam faith or leaving the city, a Jew of Cordoba, Spain in the middle of the 12th century chose the latter course. He and his family roamed for 17 years, eventually settling in Cairo, Egypt in 1165.

A member of that family was Rabbi Moses Ben Maimon (1135-1204), better known as Maimonides, a distinguished physician, theologian, and philosopher. He was an outstanding clinician who laid down rules of health which were a yardstick in medicine for centuries.

Maimonides probably acquired his medical training in Morocco during the course of his travels. In Egypt, he lectured on astronomy and Talmud philosophy, and continued as rabbi and judge. Medicine, however, proved more lucrative and he began to devote most of his time to that field. He used ancient manuscripts, supplemented with his clinical experiences and scientific deductions.

The treatises of Maimonides were written in Arabic and embraced philosophy, astronomy, mathematics, and medicine. They were a forerunner of the scientific renaissance. Three of his best known works were: (1) *Poisons and Antidotes,* a standard reference for centuries; (2) *Treatise on Hygiene,* which placed reliance upon diet and good rules of health rather than drugs; (3) *Medical Aphorisms,* based on the writings of Hippocrates, Galen, and Avicenna.

Before visiting the sick, Maimonides prayed. A portion of one of his prayers was: "Preserve my strength, Almighty Father of Mercy, that I may be able to restore the strength of the rich and the poor, the good and the bad, and friend and foe. Let me see in the sufferer the man alone. When wiser men teach me, let me be humble to learn, for the mind of man is so puny and the art of healing is so vast. But when fools are ready to advise me, let me be intent upon one thing, Father of Mercy, to be ever merciful to Thy suffering children."

He severely condemned quackery, superstition, and mysticism as medical courses. He recognized the four humors of Galen, which he blended with faith. He was honored on a stamp (Scott No. 74) issued by Israel in 1953 to commemorate the seventh International Congress For the History of Science.—Mirt, J. A.

BELGIAN PUBLIC HEALTH WORKER

Ernest Malvoz (1862-1938) graduated in medicine in 1886 from the University of Liège. He subsequently became a professor of bacteriology at the university.

In 1894 he introduced into Belgium the serum treatment of diphtheria with antitoxin. He was placed in charge of the first bacteriological institute in Belgium, where he started disinfection and water analysis services.

Malvoz established the first Belgian public sanitarium in 1897, and three years later opened the first anti-tuberculosis dispensary at Liège. Although many miners had hookworm disease, he virtually eradicated the parasitism within nine years. He also combatted miner's nystagmus. In 1912, he founded the first anti-venereal disease dispensary. Twelve years later, he established a center for the preparation and distribution of BCG vaccine against tuberculosis.

Malvoz was a sparkling enthusiast who inspired his colleagues. He died in 1938 and was honored philatelically (Scott No. B551) by Belgium in 1953; the surtax was used for anti-tuberculosis and other charitable works.—Kyle, R. A., and Shampo, M. A.

TROPICAL
MEDICINE MAN

Sir Patrick Manson (1844-1922) was born in Old-meldrum, Scotland, on Oct. 3, 1844. In his adolescent years, he did poorly in school and was apprenticed to an iron master. However, he began to show an interest in insects and worms, later studied medicine, and was graduated from the University of Aberdeen in 1865.

Manson served as a medical officer in Formosa and Amoy, China, where he saw many examples of filariasis, and is reported to have removed more than a ton of material from patients with elephantiasis. He studied the life-cycle of the *Filaria* and recognized that a mosquito was the intermediate host. He found that, amazingly, the organism appeared in the blood at sunset, but was absent during the day! He also thought that the mosquito might transmit malaria, a concept that stimulated Ross' study of malaria and mosquitoes.

Manson started a medical school in Hong Kong but later returned to London, where he founded the School of Tropical Medicine in 1899. He wrote a "Manual of Tropical Diseases," which subsequently has been republished in many editions. With the help of later editors, it has continued to be a standard text to the present time.

He accurately described sprue in 1880 and, while in China, became aware of the use of crow's liver for the treatment of anemia. He introduced smallpox vaccination to the Chinese, and also invented a trocar and cannula for the drainage of liver abscesses. Knighted in 1903, Manson became known as the "Father of Tropical Medicine." His many accomplishments were effected despite severe gout of many years' duration. Manson died in London on April 19, 1922. Although he is not honored on a postage stamp, his name appears on a Brazilian stamp (Scott No. 903) issued in 1959 honoring Dr. Pirajá da Silva and commemorating the 50th anniversary of the discovery of *Schistosoma mansoni.*—Kyle, R. A., and Shampo, M. A.

MICROSCOPIST AND HISTORIAN

Manuel Pirajá da Silva (1873-1961) was born on Jan. 28, 1873 in Camamu, Brazil, and received his medical degree from the School of Medicine of Bahia in 1896. He became a professor of clinical medical in 1902 and served in that capacity for nine years, after which he was a professor of medical history from 1911 to 1935.

Pirajá da Silva was a pioneer in the field of microscopic identification and contributed to the knowledge of intestinal schistosomiasis, amoebic dysentery, cutaneous leishmaniasis, Chagas' disease, mycoses (blastomycosis and maduromycosis), and ainhum. His most important original contribution was the discovery and identification of the *Schistosoma mansoni* (a fluke), in 1908, presenting the first complete description of the parasite.

In 1959, Brazil issued a stamp (Scott No. 903) to commemorate the 50th anniversary of the discovery and identification of *S. mansoni* by Pirajá da Silva.—Shampo, M. A., and Kyle, R. A.

NEW TRAILS IN NEUROLOGY

Georges Marinescu (1863-1938), Romanian neurologist, gained honors for his contributions to the knowledge of the anatomy, physiology, and pathology of the nervous system.

Marinescu received his MD degree from the Brancovan Hospital Medical School, Bucharest, and did postgraduate study in neurology with Charcot at the University of Paris. In 1895, he was appointed to the Chair of Clinical Neurology and in 1897 was named a professor of neurology at the University of Bucharest.

He spent 41 years in that teaching position. These were marked by extensive research and prolific writing while he became an explorer in an expanding field. He was the first (1892) to study the fatal effect of the removal of the pituitary gland in animals.

The identifying "Marinescu's sign" refers to a hand marked by edema, with lividity and coldness of the skin as seen in syringomyelia. His successes were recognized beyond the borders of Romania.

Among awards bestowed upon him were elections to the French Academy of Medicine and the Royal Society of Medicine, London. Marinescu was honored by a stamp (Scott No. 1496) issued by Romania in 1962.—Mirt, J. A., Shampo, M. A., and Kyle, R. A.

THE PLASTER MOLDED SPLINT

Many technical improvements in the care of fractures were introduced in the 19th century. The most important of these was the plaster of paris (calcium sulphate, gypsum) roller bandage (1852), invented by Anthonius Mathijsen (1805-1878), distinguished Dutch military surgeon. The new product was far more useful than the earlier resin fortified bandage.

Mathijsen, born in Budel, Holland, studied medicine at the University of Utrecht. He received his MD degree in 1837 and immediately took up an army career. His main interest was orthopedics and he carried on extensive research in that field. He was honored postally (Scott No. B134) by The Netherlands in 1941; the surtax was used for cultural and social relief.—Mirt, J. A.

MAYO CONTRIBUTIONS TO MEDICINE

Two former presidents of the American Medical Association are pictured on a 5-cent US postage stamp (Scott No. 1251) issued Sept. 11, 1964. They are Dr. William James Mayo (1861-1939) and Dr. Charles Horace Mayo (1865-1939). Both are recognized throughout the world as having been brilliant surgeons, great organizers, and esteemed leaders in medicine. Their passings were so close together that divine providence seems to have decreed as they themselves might have wished.

Being sons of the distinguished surgeon, Dr. William Worall Mayo of Rochester, Minn., it was natural for the brothers to follow in the footsteps of their father. Dr. William Mayo received his MD degree from the University of Michigan in 1883 and his younger brother from the Chicago Medical College (now part of Northwestern University) in 1888.

Dr. "Will" gave an indication of his ability when he presented his first paper, a report of an operation for ovarian tumor, before the Southern Minnesota Medical Association in 1885. This was the beginning of a flow of contributions to many phases of medical science. He showed an early interest in abdominal surgery.

Dr. "Charlie," after his graduation in medicine, returned to Rochester where his interest in research and his surgical genius led to innumerable investigations in medicine and in surgery. He, too, was a liberal contributor to medical literature.

In 1889, the elder Mayo and his sons established St. Marys Hospital in Rochester. As their fame as physicians spread, the facilities were expanded in size and broader services rendered by a steadily growing staff. The famed Mayo Clinic was in the making. Rochester, in time, changed from a small village into one of the famous medical centers of the world.

In order to assure the permanence of the institution, the Mayo brothers gave freely of their time and liberally of their funds. They established the Mayo Foundation for Medical Education and Research, affiliated with the University of Minnesota.

They not only devoted themselves to the advancement of scientific medicine but took active part in organized medicine. They headed many organizations. Dr. William J. Mayo served as president of the American Medical Association in 1906-1907, his brother occupied that position in 1916.

Such men come but infrequently in any civilization, and their places are not easily filled as the world moves on. —Mirt, J. A.

McDOWELL,
PIONEER SURGEON

On Christmas Day, 1809, a 47-year-old-woman, Mrs. Jane Todd Crawford, strapped to a wooden table in a physician's home in Danville, Ky., had a large ovarian tumor removed. In an operation which required a half hour, the physician-turned-surgeon removed a 22-pound growth. This was long before the advent of anesthesia and asepsis. The physician had only a casual medical education and no precedent to guide him. Five days later, the woman was up, and in 25 days she returned by horseback to her home 60 miles away.

There was further drama connected with this operation performed by Ephraim McDowell (1771-1830). That morning he had been denounced from the pulpit of his church, and an angry crowd gathered outside the physician's home with guns and rope. Fortunately, the woman not only came through the ordeal but lived until age 78. McDowell is said to have performed 13 operations in all, with eight recoveries. Considering the conditions under which he worked, this is a good record. Eventually, he became recognized as a skilled surgeon. His procedure is known today as "McDowell's operation."

McDowell, born in what is now Rockbridge County, Va., served as a physician's apprentice in Staunton. He went to the University of Edinburgh, Scotland to study medicine under John Bell, where he spent but part of his time on medical education. And after two years, he returned to Danville in 1795 without a degree.

Yet this did not deter him from practicing medicine, and in a short time he built up a large practice. The Medical Society of Philadelphia gave him a diploma in 1807. He received an honorary MD degree from the University of Maryland in 1825.

McDowell's portrait appears on a 4c postage stamp (Scott No. 1138) issued in 1959 by the United States.— Mirt, J. A.

MONK CONTRIBUTES TO GENETICS

Gregor Mendel (1822-1884) was born in Heinzendorf in Moravia on July 22, 1822. His peasant family devoted itself to gardening, and he naturally developed a love of plants. His mother wanted him to have a higher station in life, and his family made many sacrifices to send him to school. They became unable to support him financially, and in order to continue his studies, he entered the Augustine order as a novice in 1843. He was given the name Gregor, which he used for the rest of his life.

Being interested in science, Mendel was assigned as a teacher of physics in one of the secondary schools of the order. Later he taught zoology, botany, and physics in a technical high school. On two occasions, he failed to obtain his teacher's certificate, and had to continue as an assistant teacher. His classic experiments with peas were begun in a little garden 35 meters long and 7 meters wide in which he discovered the laws of independent segregation and independent assortment accepted today as common knowledge.

Mendel was interested in flowers and worked with 30 different species of plants. In addition, he planted many fruit trees, and was a well-known bee keeper. He made daily meteorological observations for many years. Eventually he became head of the monastery. This required much administrative time and he was not able to follow his scientific pursuits. Also, he had many difficulties with governmental officials who wanted to tax his order's property.

Mendel died Jan. 6, 1884, of chronic glomerulone-phritis. After his funeral, his associates set aside all his well-bound books for the monastery library and burned everything else. Thus, all original records of his work were lost except two brief published contributions ignored until 1900. Postally, he was honored by Danzig (Scott No. 238) in 1939.—Kyle, R. A., and Shampo, M. A.

MENDELEEV — PEER OF RUSSIAN CHEMISTS

The periodic law of the classification of chemical elements, worked out by Dmitri Lvanovich Mendeleev (1834-1907), has become an integral part of modern chemistry. Indirectly, it has a bearing on medical research.

Mendeleev, widely regarded as the peer of Russian chemists, proved that a periodic repetition of the properties of chemicals is obtained if all of the elements are arranged by their atomic weight. From this thesis, he derived the law that the properties of elements are a periodic function of the atomic weight.

And he grouped the elements into nine classes—possessing similar or recurring properties.

This system, while not perfect, was instrumental in predicting the discovery and properties of new elements. He left empty spaces for elements not yet discovered. These were filled in eventually through subsequent findings by others.

Mendeleev was born in Tobolsk, Siberia and studied the natural sciences at the University of St. Petersburg (now Leningrad) and the University of Heidelberg, Germany. He was appointed Professor of Chemistry at the University of St. Petersburg in 1866. His "Elements of Chemistry" became a standard textbook.

His portrait appears on Russian (Scott Nos. 536-539, 1577, 1906) and Polish (Scott No. 881) postage stamps. —Mirt, J. A.

ZOOLOGIST STUDENT
OF PHAGOCYTOSIS

Elie Metchnikoff (1845-1916) was born on May 16, 1845, at Ivanovka near Kharkov, Russia, where his father was an officer in the Imperial Guard. He completed his degree at the University of Kharkov and in 1864 went to Germany. He wrote many papers, discussing such topics as rotifers, marine animals, microscopic animals, and cockroaches. He is considered to be one of the two men who established the field of cellular embryology. His contributions were based on his many papers from 1875 to 1886. And his work soon brought renown.

Metchnikoff was best known for his studies of phagocytosis which began in Messina in 1882. He thought that phagocytes removed both dead and injured tissue and played an important part in immunity and resistance to disease. He discounted the role of humoral antibodies, which led to many arguments with the "humoralists." Invited to the Pasteur Institute in Paris in 1888, he continued his study of phagocytosis. And in 1908, he received the Nobel Prize for his research in immunity.

Metchnikoff thought that unhealthy fermentation in the large intestine produced poisons which in turn caused deterioration of the arteries, senility and early death. He advocated a diet that contained bacilli-producing lactic acid. He, himself, drank a pint of sour milk daily. He was an advocate of the long-disproved idea of intestinal intoxication. Critics calling him a "modern Ponce de Leon" mused that he found his fountain of youth in milky whey!

Metchnikoff transferred syphilis from chimpanzee to chimpanzee. He apparently discovered spirochetes years before they were described by Schaudin but did not recognize their etiologic significance.

He contracted bronchitis, pneumonia and pleurisy, and died on July 15, 1916. Postmortem examination showed atheroma of the aorta and related cardiac disease. His body was cremated and an urn containing the ashes placed in the library of the Pasteur Institute. He has been philatelically honored by France (Scott No. B398) in 1966 and by Russia in 1945 (Scott Nos. 1011-1012) and in 1963 (Scott No. 2803).—Kyle, R. A., and Shampo, M. A.

BEGINNINGS OF PSYCHIATRY

Austria's status in surgery and medical education in the last half of the 19th century was advanced by contributions of the German-born Theodor Hermann Meynert (1833-1892). As a neurologist and psychiatrist, he did extensive research into the anatomy and physiology of the brain.

Meynert was born in Dresden, Germany, and received his medical education at the University of Vienna. His interest early turned to a study of the nervous system. He was appointed a professor of neurology and psychiatry by his alma mater in 1873, holding the position for the remainder of his life. Physicians and students came from all parts of the world to learn from him.

His name is linked with anatomical discoveries in neurology and physiology. "Meynert's bundle" is a description of the fasciculus retroflexus. "Meynert's commissure" is a tract of nerve fibers. The "solitary cells of Meynert" are located in the cerebral cortex in the region of the calcarine fissure.

Among his contributions to medical literature was *Disease of the Forebrain* (1884). He edited the *Yearbook of Psychiatry* from 1889 until his death. He also founded an institution for the insane near Vienna.

Meynert's portrait appears on an Austrian postage stamp (Scott No. B164) issued in 1937 to honor famous Austrian physicians.—Mirt, J. A.

FRENCH MICROBIOLOGIST

Charles Henri Nicolle (1866-1936), French bacteriologist, won the 1928 Nobel Prize in Medicine for creating a typhus vaccine.

Nicolle was born in Rouen, France, the son of a physician. After his graduation in medicine from the University of Paris, he served as an assistant professor at the Rouen School of Medicine. In 1903, he was named Director of the Pasteur Institute in Tunis, and also served as a surgeon in the French Army.

In 1909, he reported that typhus germs are transmitted through lice. This led to further researches and the discovery of a vaccine that gave promise of wiping out the plague of typhus. He also studied relapsing fever and kala-azar. Nicolle was a member of the French Academy of Sciences and of the French Academy of Medicine and a professor of the College of France. He was honored by France on a stamp (Scott No. 867) featuring the famous physician in 1958.—Mirt, J. A.

NURSING AS PROFESSION

Wounded British soldiers in the Crimean War (1854-1856) looked forward to visits by "The Lady with the Lamp." Her administrations eased pains and gave hope. Today, in nurse capping exercises, graduates carry a symbolical lit candle.

Florence Nightingale (1820-1910) was born in Florence, Italy, during a visit there by her English parents. She was named for the city of her birth. During her lifetime, nursing was considered a menial occupation for her station in life. Furthermore, there was no school for training women in England in the mid-19th century. And in 1850 she went to Düsseldorf, Germany for training. After her graduation, she returned to England. In 1853, she became superintendent of the Hospital for Invalid Gentlewomen in London. Through her efforts, a nursing school and home for nurses was established at St. Thomas Hospital in 1860. This became a pattern for others that followed.

Early in the Crimean War, the deplorable facilities for the care of the wounded became evident. Under her direction, a small staff of nurses went to Scutari. Within a few months, the military hospital wards were clean and efficient. She made her rounds by the light of a lamp she carried. She returned to London after the war and was the first woman to receive the British Order of Merit. She has been honored postally many times. Her portrait is seen on a stamp (Scott No. 209) issued by Dominica in 1968, to commemorate the International Human Rights Year.—Mirt, J. A.

VETERINARIAN CONTRIBUTES TO MEDICINE

Edmond Isidore Etiènne Nocard (1850-1903) was born in Provins, France, on January 29, 1850. He studied veterinary medicine at the Alfort Veterinary College and ultimately was made director of the school in 1887.

He is remembered mainly for his work with actinomycosis in animals. Nocardiasis, an infection caused by an aerobic actinomycete, may produce pulmonary abscesses or a granulomatous infection limited to the foot (maduromycosis). Nocard's interests included the relationship of tuberculosis in animals to that in man, as he believed that tuberculosis was the same in all species. He thought that mastitis in cattle was caused by streptococci, and recognizing that the disease was transmitted to healthy cows by the milker, he outlined a prophylactic program. He also made extensive studies of the bulbar lesions of rabies, anthrax, tetanus, cholera, and glanders. He was associated with Emile Roux for many years.

Nocard died on August 2, 1903, and was honored philatelically by France for his contributions to veterinary medicine. His portrait is shown on a 1951 French stamp (Scott No. 655) with those of Henri Marie Bouley and Jean Baptiste August Chauveau.—Kyle, R. A., and Shampo, M. A.

JAPANESE AMERICAN
MICROBIOLOGIST

The diversity of the interests of Hideyo Noguchi (1876-1928), Japanese-born microbiologist who spent most of his brilliant scientific career in the United States, platters in the air at the same time. He displayed great industry and always was a master craftsman in developing devices and techniques, rarely a slave to procedure.

Noguchi, born in a small Japanese village, studied at the Kitasato Institute of Infectious Diseases in Tokyo. He came to Philadelphia in 1899 at the invitation of Simon Flexner. When the latter was appointed Director of the newly formed Rockefeller Institute for Medical Research in New York, Noguchi went along and became a full member of the Institute in 1914.

Snake venom was the principal subject of Noguchi's research in the first decade of his life in the United States. The peak of his career was reached in the second decade when his interest turned to spirochetes. In that field, he developed a test for tabes based on the increase of protein in the cerebrospinal fluid and proposed a modification of the Wasserman test for syphilis. He was also interested in poliomyelitis, rabies, and trachoma.

The third decade of his life was marked by eagerness to develop new vistas in medical science. He traveled throughout the southwestern United States to study trachoma, went to Peru to examine Oroya fever, to other parts of South America, and to Africa to study the pathogenesis of yellow fever.

Noguchi's last endeavor was responsible for his becoming a martyr to medical science. He died of yellow fever in what is now Ghana. Japan, which he visited on numerous occasions, honored his memory with an 8-yen stamp (Scott No. 480) in 1949.—Mirt, J. A., Kyle, R. A., and Shampo, M. A.

PHYSICIAN BOTANIST
IN TROPICAL MEDICINE

In 1964, Portugal honored one of her most famous sons, Garcia da Orta, by issuing a series of postage stamps (Scott Nos. 922-924) in his honor. The occasion was the 400th anniversary of the publication of his remarkable work "Coloquios," which catalogued, discussed, evaluated, and detailed the method of cultivations of many tropical plants then unknown to Europeans. He was the first to describe Asiatic cholera and its manifestations, and also the first to perform an autopsy on an Indian subject with this disease. He has been called the "Father of Pharmacognosy."

Garcia da Orta was born in the small Portuguese town of Elvas in 1490. He studied at the famous Spanish universities of Salamanca and Alcalá de Henares and he received his MD degree. However, he returned to Portugal in 1523 to become an assistant professor of natural philosophy at the University of Lisbon. Again he left Portugal, in 1534, and traveled extensively, collecting his material for the "Coloquios."

The "Coloquios" consists of 57 colloquies, or chapters, on a similar number of drugs or spices, mostly of vegetable origin, but also including substances such as ivory, diamonds, and bezoarstone. The work was considered a landmark in the history of materia medica. The items discussed by da Orta are of two types, first those associated in the materia medica and botany of India, and second, the description and treatment of certain diseases.

145

Da Orta died in 1568 and was honored on a stamp (Scott No. 466) bearing his portrait issued by Portuguese India in 1946.—Shampo, M. A., and Kyle, R. A.

MEDICINE IN
EL SALVADOR

A monument of Tomás Garcia Palomo (1856-1921) standing in front of the Medical School of the University of San Salvador is a testimony to his accomplishments as a physician and statesman.

Palomo received his MD degree from the university at the age of 24 and soon became associated with the surgical department of Rosales Hospital. He maintained that affiliation throughout the four decades of his medical career. As physician-in-chief, he was instrumental in introducing x-ray equipment into El Salvador.

Palomo also served as a professor of medicine at his alma mater, president of the Public Health Council, and minister of state. He was honored on a stamp (Scott No. 563) issued by El Salvador in 1935.—Mirt, J. A.

PARACELSUS —
CONTROVERSIAL FIGURE

Philippus Aureolus Theophrastus Bombastus von Hohenheim (1493-1541), a German, was popularly known by his adopted name as Paracelsus, derived from the name of Celsus, physician of the first century A.D. Celsus had been a Roman medical encyclopedist who described the four classical signs of inflammation: heat, pain, redness, and swelling.

Paracelsus was a rebel, the "beatnik" of his period, an intellectual vagabond who aroused much antagonism. He was part of the 16th century ferment which slowly transformed medieval mystic attitudes to 17th century materialism.

Paracelsus was born near Zürich and inherited his interest in medicine from his father, a practicing physician. He showed a deep interest in philosophy. After studying medicine at the University of Ferrara in Italy, he traveled widely throughout Europe and the Middle East acquiring knowledge of a great variety of diseases. He formalized his own materia medica and developed his own therapy.

Paracelsus attacked all medical authorities with the exception of Hippocrates. He was especially concerned with the destruction of the Aristotelian and Galenian principles of medieval medicine. Among his greatest contributions were the introduction of biochemical analysis and of the use of numerous metals in medicine. His separation of coagulum from urine anticipated the discovery of albumin. He suggested that there was acid in the stomach. He was the first to note the coincidence of cretinism and endemic goiter. He warned against stress— "four things you should avoid are strong flavored wines, rich food, anger, and women."—He was honored by a German stamp (Scott No. B311) issued in 1949. The surtax was given to welfare organizations.—Mirt, J. A.

FOREMOST SURGEON OF
THE SIXTEENTH CENTURY

Ambroise Paré (1510-1590), a barber's apprentice with a scanty education, became one of the greatest surgeons of his time. He gained fame as an army surgeon, introducing many new concepts. His faith in the healing power of nature resulted in his dropping some of the long-standing forms of treatment, particularly in the care of gunshot wounds. He substituted ligature for cautery in vascular surgery, and made important contributions to obstetrics and syphilology as well. He recorded his observations in great detail.

In the Huguenot massacre of 1572, his life was spared by order of the king who took him into his palace. He was honored on a stamp (Scott No. B163) issued by France in 1943 to honor famous 16th century Frenchmen. The surtax was used for national relief.—Mirt, J. A.

PASTEUR

Louis Pasteur (1822-1895) was born on December 27, 1822 in Jura, France. He had an early interest in art but turned to science and received his baccalaureate in science in 1842. Ironically, he received a mediocre grade in chemistry. He studied at L'École Normale and at the Sorbonne, and passed his examinations in chemistry and physics.

In 1848, he reported that tartaric acid crystallizes in two chemically identical but physically different forms—levo or dextro—based on rotation of light passing through the material. This study opened the field of stereochemistry. Pasteur began studies of fermentation of sugar to form alcohol and found that micro-organisms were responsible. He observed that germs were present in air, and his studies refuted the old theory of spontaneous generation and became the basis of the "germ theory." He developed the process now known as pasteurization, for the purpose of protecting wines from damage. He also investigated and established the causation of two diseases which had been ravaging the silkworms and destroying the silk industry in France.

Nine years before his death Pasteur suffered a stroke, weakening his left arm and leg. This occurred about two years after Pasteur and Roux had developed a vaccine against rabies from brain tissue.

In 1885, Pasteur vaccinated a 9-year-old boy (Joseph Meister, who later worked at the Pasteur Institute) who had been bitten 14 times by a rabid dog. This led to vaccination of 350 persons, only one of whom developed rabies.

Pasteur became Director of the Pasteur Institute in 1888, and died on September 28, 1895 of a cerebrovascular accident. He was given a state funeral and his body was placed in a marble crypt in the small chapel within the Institute. He was honored philatelically by Poland in 1959 (Scott No. 883).—Kyle, R. A., and Shampo, M. A.

PHYSIOLOGIST
EXTRAORDINARY

Ivan Petrovich Pavlov (1849-1936), Russian physiologist, was an outstanding contributor to the medical knowledge of cardiac and digestive physiology, of the central nervous system, and of psychophysiology.

Russian psychological medicine and much of Russian general medicine are firmly based on Pavlovian theory and research, although western medicine ignores his mechanistic approach to healing. Much of his research work was carried out at the Imperial Academy of Sciences and Imperial Institute of Experimental Medicine in St. Petersburg. Through the development of an experimental technique of "sham feeding" of animals, he discovered the reflex relationship of the nervous system to the digestive tract.

He received honorary degrees from the universities of Edinburgh and Paris, was elected to the Royal Society of London, and received the Nobel Prize in Physiology and Medicine in 1904. Postally, he has been honored by Argentina, Romania, Russia, and Sweden. His portrait is shown on the stamp (Scott No. 684) issued by Argentina in 1959.—Mirt, J. A.

BACTERIOLOGIST
PLAGUE VICTIM

Portugal, in December 1966, issued a postage stamp (Scott No. 983) portraying a graduate of the University of Lisbon Medical School. Camara Pestana (1863-1899) was a bacteriologist and a martyr to medical science.

He was born in Funchal, Madeira. After receiving his MD degree, he became associated with the Lisbon Municipal Laboratory. He studied bacteriology at the Pasteur Institute in Paris. In 1892, he returned to Lisbon to become director of the newly organized Bacteriological Institute. During the plague of 1899, he became mortally infected in the performance of an autopsy.—Mirt, J. A.

TUBERCULOSIS
PREVENTION
IN SCOTLAND

Robert William Philip (1857-1939) was graduated with honors in medicine by the University of Edinburgh, Scotland, in 1882, the year that Robert Koch announced the discovery of the tubercle bacillus. Philip spent his life in studying tuberculosis and its related diseases. He experimented on animals with sterilized tuberculous sputum which proved to be toxic. He was one of the first to realize the importance of preventing infection. He investigated conditions under which families lived, and taught them how to avoid infection. His system of open air treatment of tuberculosis in all stages was contrary to the then practice of keeping the patient free from drafts.

Over the years Philip developed what became known as the "Edinburgh Plan." This eventually covered Scotland with a network of hospitals for persons with advanced tuberculosis, sanitariums, open air schools, and farm colonies for those on the road to recovery.

After this program had become widely established, Philip attacked the milk problem. He had found (in 1920) that some of the milk was contaminated with tubercle bacilli. Leasing a farm, he demonstrated an efficient method of aseptic production and handling of milk. Meanwhile, he had been elected to the first Chair of

Tuberculosis at the University of Glasgow. Clinical teaching and a course of lectures in tuberculosis became compulsory in the medical curriculum. He was knighted in 1913 and received the Trudeau Medal of the American Tuberculosis Association in 1928.

Belgium (Scott No. B585) recognized Philip with philatelic honors in 1955.—Mirt, J. A.

REPUBLIQUE·FRANÇAISE

8F

P
O
S
T
E
S

PINEL
1745-1826

EIGHTEENTH CENTURY PSYCHIATRIST

Late in the 18th century, Philippe Pinel (1745-1826), introduced a new concept in the treatment of the mentally ill. This "father of psychiatry," against strong medical and political opposition, theorized that insanity, like many other afflictions, had an organic cause.

Pinel urged investigation of bodily changes responsible for deranged minds, that various abnormalities be analyzed, that a distinction be made between the lunatic and the depraved, and that methods be developed to improve the lot of these unfortunates.

His opportunity to test this theory came later when he was placed in charge of the Bicêtre, a combination prison and insane asylum for men. Over considerable objection, he unchained the prisoners and allowed them freedom within the institution. The predicted maniacal outburst failed to materialize. Those able to work were given useful employment and in time many were released. He put into effect a recording of case histories, and did systematic research. As administrator of Salpêtrière, an asylum for demented women, he continued his investigations with surprisingly favorable results. Pinel's initiative paved the way for further attacks on the problem by Charcot, Freud, and others.

Pinel, born in St. André d'Alayrac, France, originally studied for the priesthood but switched to medicine, the profession of his father and paternal grandfather. He received his MD in 1773 at the University of Toulouse.

After moving to Paris in 1778, he did tutoring, writing, and translating, in the course of which he visited a private hospital where he witnessed the treatment of the insane. The inhumanity appalled him. In 1794, he was appointed a professor of medicine in a newly opened medical school, a post which he held until 1822 when he was dismissed because of his liberal views.

Pinel continued to work until he suffered an incapacitating cerebral hemorrhage in 1823. He died three years later. His gift to mankind was a new branch of medicine, psychiatry. He was honored by a French stamp (Scott No. 865) issued in 1958.—Mirt, J. A.

DA GAMA PINTO

Caetano Antonio Da Gama Pinto (1853-1945), Portuguese ophthalmologist, made a name for himself as a medical educator as well as an expert in his field.

Da Gama Pinto was born near New Goa, Portuguese India, which was seized by India in 1961. He received his MD degree from the University of Lisbon in 1878 and did postgraduate studies at the University of Heidelberg, Germany.

Upon his return to Portugal, he was appointed a professor of ophthalmology on the Faculty of Medicine, University of Lisbon. He later also served in the same capacity in New Goa. Medical literature was enriched by his writings on diseases of the eye.

Da Gama Pinto is pictured on two postage stamps of Portuguese India (Scott Nos. 528, 529) issued in 1954 on the centenary of his birth.—Mirt, J. A.

MILITARY PHYSICIAN

Nikolai I. Pirogov (1810-1881) is considered the most important figure in Russian military medical history. He received his MD degree from the University of Moscow in 1832, followed by two years of study in Berlin. After teaching five years at the University of Dorpat, Pirogov became professor of surgery in the Military Medical Academy (now Kirov Medical Institute of Leningrad). The study of gangrene attracted his attention, and he initiated the isolation of patients. That the disease was produced by microbes was then unknown to him or his colleagues. He studied the course of gangrene, performed countless autopsies, and did animal experimentation. Finally, he arrived at the conclusion that gangrene was caused by unknown living organisms. His book, *Elements of Field Surgery* (1863), laid groundwork of military field surgery based on the cleanliness of wards, operating rooms, and clothing. His name is associated with amputation of the foot at the ankle. In 1960, Russia issued a stamp (Scott No. 2401) in his honor.—Mirt, J. A.

DISCOVERY OF ANAPHYLAXIS

Paul Jones Portier (1866-1962), a French biologist and bacteriologist, was born in Bar-sur-Sein, Aube, France, in 1866. He was a doctor of medicine, a doctor of science, a teacher of comparative physiology at the University of Paris, and an instructor in the physiology of marine animals at the Oceanographic Institute.

Together with Charles Robert Richet, Portier discovered the anaphylactic reaction in 1901 while a member of a scientific expedition conducted by Prince Albert I of Monaco to the Azores and Cape Verde Islands. From 1912 to 1936, he was a professor of science at the University of Paris. He also was a member of the Academy of Sciences. During World War II, he served as Director of Research Laboratories for National Defense of France and was also elected to membership in the Academy of Medicine.

His best known works were *les Symbiotes* (1918) and *Physiologie des animaux marines* (1938). He died in Bourg-la-Reine in 1962 and has been honored by a set of three stamps issued by Monaco (Scott Nos. 303, 304, 305). The stamps show *Physalia* and the laboratory ship *Hirondelle II,* plus the portraits of Portier, Richet, and Albert I, and were issued in 1953 to commemorate the 50th anniversary of the discovery of anaphylaxis.—Shampo, M. A., and Kyle, R. A.

FIRST TO STUDY
FINGERPRINTS

Jan Evangelista Purkyne (or Purkinje) (1787-1869), Bohemian physiologist, was a pioneer in the use of the microtome and contributed materially to microbiological knowledge. He also was the first to point out the characteristics and importance of fingerprints (1823), but his recommendation for a system of classification was ignored.

His research in physiological optics produced a method of lighting the retina and measuring the curvature of the lens and cornea. This led Helmholtz to the invention of the ophthalmoscope. The name of Purkyne is linked with numerous medical eponyms; cells with large branching neurons in the middle layer of the cerebellar cortex; beaded muscular fibers forming a network in the subendocardial tissue of the ventricle of the heart; an image upon the retina produced by the shadow of the blood vessels; the network of immature muscle fibers in the subendocardial tissue of the ventricles of the heart, and the phenomenon that fields of equal brightness but different color are unequally bright if the intensity of the illumination is increased.

Purkyne received his MD degree from the University of Prague in 1819. With the help of Goethe, he obtained an appointment as a professor of physiology and pathology at the University of Breslau against the opposition of the faculty. There he worked in a hostile atmosphere. But, in time, his discoveries won the admiration of his detractors. He remained at Breslau until 1850, when he was called to the University of Prague. He was honored postally (Scott Nos. 232 and 233) by Czechoslovakia in 1937.—Mirt, J. A., Shampo, M. A., and Kyle, R. A.

FIRST CAESAREAN
IN SOUTH AMERICA

A painting in the Colombian room of the International College of Surgeons, Chicago, was reproduced on an 80c Colombian postage stamp issued in 1967.

The painting shows Josè Ignacio Quevedo Amaya (third from left, holding the baby) surrounded by physicians and nurse, performing the first Caesarean section in South America in 1844. Both mother and child are reported to have survived the operation, with the son living to be 80 years of age.

Quevedo was born of Spanish parents in Bogota, Colombia. He was also personal physician to General Santander, Colombian liberator. After the latter's death, Quevedo moved to Medellin, Colombia, where he founded the Academy of Medicine. In 1860, he performed a resection of the tibia, the first of its kind in Colombia.

The stamp which was issued to commemorate the centenary of the National University of Bogota (Scott No. C493) also shows the escutcheon of the Colombian College of Surgeons. The painting was made in 1954 by Enrique Grau for the International College of Surgeons.—Mirt, J. A., Shampo, M. A., and Kyle, R. A.

EARLY MEDICINE IN CUBA

The name of Tomás Romay Chacon (1764-1849), Cuban pathologist, placed medicine in Cuba on a scientific plane through the introduction of new European techniques of which he was a pioneer in his country.

Romay was born in Havana and initially prepared for a law career. However, he changed his mind, took up medicine, and received his MD degree from the University of Havana in 1791. Four years later, he was appointed to the Chair of Pathology, a position which he occupied until his death.

Word of the successful use of vaccine by Edward Jenner as a preventive of smallpox reached Cuba shortly after the opening of the 19th century. In 1804, Romay introduced the practice in Cuba.

Romay was a factor in many other phases of the health of Cubans. He was influential in setting up the first medical examining board, the death of which coincided with his own. Burial in churches was the practice at that time, but he worked for the establishment of cemeteries as a more sanitary place of repose for the dead. Among his other introductions were autopsies in medical education and a medical library. And he managed a hospital for mental defectives for five years.

Romay's portrait appears on a Cuban stamp (Scott No. 599) issued in 1958.—Mirt, J. A.

NEUROANATOMIST

Santiago Ramón y Cajal (1852-1934) was born on May 1, 1852, in Petilla, Spain. As a preparatory school pupil he was a dismal failure and was apprenticed first to a barber and later to a cobbler. He was much more interested in the out-of-doors, and particularly in art. His father became a professor of anatomy at the University of Zaragoza, and together the father and son studied anatomy. Ramón y Cajal received his MD from the University of Zaragoza, was drafted into the Spanish Army, and served in Cuba where he suffered from malaria and dysentery. Returning to Spain, he was appointed an assistant in anatomy in Zaragoza and purchased a microscope and a microtome to begin his work. He contracted tuberculosis in 1878 but recovered after a period of rest. He became a professor of histology at the University of Barcelona.

He improved Golgi's chrome silver stain for nerve tissue and then began a systematic study of the entire nervous system. His skill in drawing was of great help to him in his work. He developed a silver nitrate stain that showed nerve cells and fibers with clarity. Subsequently, he used a gold stain for astrocytes. "Cajal's stain," using potassium bichromate and osmic acid, stains nerve cells black and neuroglia cells a reddish black.

His major contribution was the developmental and structural basis of the dynamics of the neuron, of transmission of nerve impulses, and degeneration and regeneration of the nervous system. He published more than 250 papers. Ramón y Cajal was awarded the Nobel Prize in Physiology and Medicine with Golgi in 1906. This was the first time a histologist had received this prize. He continued his work until his death on Oct. 17, 1934. He was honored on a stamp (Scott No. 793) issued by Spain in 1952.—Mirt, J. A.

VETERINARIAN AND BACTERIOLOGIST

Veterinary schools have produced numerous scientists whose discoveries have been a boon to mankind. An outstanding example was Gaston Léon Ramon (1885-1963), French bacteriologist, who developed vaccines against diphtheria and tetanus.

Ramon received his DVM degree from the Alfort School of Veterinary Medicine, Paris in 1910. He became an assistant to Pierre Paul Émile Roux at the Pasteur Institute in Paris. Ramon was assigned to a serum farm where horses were inoculated in the production of diphtheria and tetanus antitoxins. In this work, he independently developed vaccines against those diseases.

Receiving only discouraging advice from Roux concerning a large scale production of the vaccines, Ramon had a Canadian laboratory produce the vaccines. As their use increased, the merits became apparent. The vaccines proved especially effective during World War II.

Many honors were conferred upon Ramon, including the Medal of the French Legion of Honor and election to the French Academy of Medicine and French Academy of Sciences. He served as Director of the Pasteur Institute of Paris in 1939-1941, and wrote hundreds of articles for scientific journals.

In May 1967, four years after his sudden death, France issued a postage stamp (Scott No. 1183) bearing his portrait and the gateway to the two-century-old School of Veterinary Medicine (Maison-Alfort).—Mirt, J. A.

AMERICAN MILITARY SURGEON
AND MICROBIOLOGIST

At the turn of the 20th century, an American commission headed by Major Walter Reed (1851-1902) was sent to Cuba to look into the problem of yellow fever. It found that a filtrable virus, transmitted by the mosquito *Aëdes aegypti* was responsible. Mosquito control was the answer, and the commission findings had far-reaching effects throughout the world.

Reed was born in Gloucester County, Va., the son of an itinerant minister. He received his MD from the University of Virginia Medical School at Charlottesville, subsequently a second degree from the Bellevue Hospital Medical College, New York. He practiced for a while before he received a commission as first lieutenant in the Army in 1875.

After serving at a medical post in Arizona, he was ordered in 1890 to the Johns Hopkins University in Baltimore for study in bacteriology and pathology. Three years later, as major, he was assigned to the post of professor of bacteriology and clinical microscopy in the newly organized Army Medical School in Washington—a postgraduate training unit.

With the outbreak of the Spanish-American War in 1898, he was named chairman of a committee to study the cause and propagation of typhoid fever. He presented evidence that the disease was spread in army camps by the common fly.

Reed's last and most significant army assignment was to determine the method by which yellow fever was transmitted. He headed a commission to Cuba in 1900. With the aid of Carlos Finlay, who had advanced the mosquito transmission theory of the disease, Reed undertook a series of experiments with controls. A group of volunteers allowed themselves to be bitten by infected *Aëdes aegypti* and in due time came down with the disease. With the mode of transmittal established, the way was cleared for preventive measures through mosquito control.

Reed returned to Washington as pathology and bacteriology professor at the Army Medical School and Columbia Medical School (now George Washington Medical School). He died from a periappendiceal abscess. Walter Reed Hospital in the nation's capital is a memorial to America's greatest military surgeon. His portrait is shown on a stamp (Scott No. 877) of the Famous American Series issued by the U.S.A. in 1940.—Mirt, J. A.

ARABIAN PHYSICIAN

Rhazes Mohammed Ibn Zakariya Pazi, also called Rhazes (ca. 860-932 A.D.), was born in Raj, Persia. He was the chief physician at the leading hospital in Bagdad and was a court physician. He was the author of more than 140 medical works, including a general treatise (in 10 books, translated into Latin, circa 1485) that greatly influenced medical science in the Middle Ages. Rhazes was the first to describe and write about the differential diagnosis between measles and smallpox, and he introduced such drugs as mercury compounds and lead ointment. He is also credited with being the first to use sutures from animal gut.

In 1964, Iran issued two stamps (Scott Nos. 1312-1313) to commemorate the anniversary of his birth. The Syrian Arab Republic also honored him philatelically in 1968.—Shampo, M. A., and Kyle, R. A.

PHYSIOLOGIST, PATHOLOGIST, PHYSICIAN

In 1901, Albert I, ruler of the principality of Monaco and one of the world's most noted oceanographers, sent his laboratory-equipped yacht on an expedition to the waters around the Azores and Cape Verde Islands. The members included two famous French scientists, Richet and Portier.

The scientists were doing research on the toxin contained in the filaments of the *Physalia* (Portuguese man-of-war). They then studied a toxin from sea anemones and found that dogs which received the toxin became very sensitive to small second doses and many died. This was called anaphylaxis, the reverse of prophylaxis or immunity. The discovery of anaphylaxis shed new light on diseases such as hay fever, asthma, drug reactions, and serum sickness. For this, Charles Robert Richet (1850-1935), French physiologist, received the 1913 Nobel Prize in Medicine.

Richet was born in Paris on Aug. 26, 1850, the son of Alfred Richet, a well-known surgeon. He received his MD degree in 1877, but earlier had studied conditioned reflexes in the digestive process and observed that the acid of gastric juice was hydrochloric acid. In 1881, he was appointed co-director of the *Revûe Scientifique,* and in 1887 he became a professor of physiology in the Faculty of Medicine of the University of Paris. He worked on the physiology of respiration and on epilepsy.

Richet made outstanding contributions in many fields —physiology, bacteriology, pathology, psychology, and medical statistics. In addition, he was an orator, an ardent peace worker, a poet, novelist, and playwright. He died in 1935 and was honored on a 1953 stamp of Monaco with Albert I of Monaco and Portier, for his work in anaphylaxis (Scott Nos. 303, 304, 305).—Shampo, M. A., and Kyle, R. A.

ANTHROPOLOGY AND MEDICINE

Paul Rivet (1876-1958), French physician, had a notable career in medicine, anthropology, ethnology, and politics over a half century.

After receiving his MD degree in 1897 from the École du Service de Santé Militaire, of Lyon, he studied further for a year at Val de Grace Military Medical Center at Sindes, near Paris. In 1901, he was assigned by the French Medical Corps to accompany a geodetic survey to Ecuador. On this five-year tour of duty, he became interested in anthropology and ethnology. After returning to Paris in 1906, he set up a laboratory for anthropology in the National Museum. He became deputy director three years later.

In World War I, Rivet directed the Bureau of Hygiene and Epidemiologic Services of the Allied Armies. He worked out a program of malaria control in the armed forces. For these services, he was awarded the Croix de Guerre and the Gold Medal des Epidémies.

Rivet became secretary of the Institute of Ethnology at the University of Paris in 1926, and three years later was appointed a professor of anthropology. In 1938, he dedicated the celebrated Museum of Humanity. When the invading German army neared Paris in World War II, he fled to Bogota, Colombia, where he established a counterpart of the French Museum.

After the liberation of France, Rivet returned to Paris. There, he added politics to his activities. His important posts included the presidency of the Supreme Council. Rivet is pictured on an Ecuador air mail stamp (Scott No. 340) issued nine months after his death.—Mirt, J. A.

GUATEMALAN PHYSICIAN
ENTERS POLITICS

Valverde Rodolfo Robles (1878-1939) was born on Jan. 14, 1878, in Quezaltenango, Guatemala, and studied medicine at the University of California, National Institute of Quezaltenango, and the Faculty of Medicine in Paris. He received his medical degree from the last named in 1904. An outstanding and most versatile physician and scientist, Robles was also conversant in many languages. He was a member of the Faculty of Medicine in Guatemala, a leading surgeon, and was made Dean of the Faculty of Science (1916) and Head of the Department of Sanitation (1918).

Observing that many people became blind from subcutaneous nodules around the eye, he identified the etiologic agent as *Filaria* and called this disease "pseudoleprosy," naming its causative parasite "Onchocerca Robles *(O. volvulus)*." This remains his eponym and he described it in detail in 1917 as onchocercosis.

For approximately 20 years, he was attached to the Guatemalan Legation in Paris, and for nine years, he was Deputy of the Guatemalan Congress. In 1928, he was given the degree of Doctor of Hygiene. Robles was also a member of many societies in Paris and London and was a Chevalier and Officer of the Legion of Honor. He died in 1939 and was honored by Guatemalan stamp (Scott No. C260) in 1962.—Shampo, M. A., and Kyle, R. A.

X-RAYS

Wilhelm Konrad Röntgen (1845-1923) was born on March 27, 1845, in Lennep, Germany. He grew up in Holland and received a degree in mechanical engineering in Zürich, Switzerland. He received his PhD degree in 1869 based on his studies in gases at the University of Zürich—although he had never had a basic college course in physics!

Röntgen did extensive research on the measurement of minute quantities of substances and of changes in their temperature due to altered physical conditions. He became interested in electricity and measured magnetic effects produced when a glass plate was moved between two electrically-charged plates. He was fascinated by cathode rays and noted that a screen coated with barium platino-cyanide fluoresced.

On Nov. 8, 1895, Röntgen found that this phenomenon was not due to the cathode rays but was from a new ray, which he called x-ray (he noted that these x-rays would show the bones in a person's hand). Subsequently, these were called roentgen rays. He received the Nobel Prize in Physics in 1901. He continued to work in the laboratory and died of cancer of the gastrointestinal tract on Feb. 10, 1923. He was honored philatelically in 1939 by Danzig (Scott No. 240).—Kyle, R. A., Shampo, M. A., and Mirt, J. A.

KARL FREIHERR v ROKITANSKY
1804 1878
S 1.50
REPUBLIK ÖSTERREICH

PATHOLOGIST
EXTRAORDINARY

Human dissection reached its pinnacle under Carl Freiherr von Rokitansky (1804-1878), Austrian pathfinder in pathology. In a period of 40 years, he personally performed more than 30,000 autopsies and had access to reports of another 40,000. All this was possible because permission of kin was not necessary, once a person was admitted to a hospital in Vienna where Rokitansky was a professor of Pathology at the University. From this vast fund of information and research, he was able to publish many professional papers on various problems of anatomical pathology.

His work established a basis for scientific medicine, which has developed with far-reaching influence. He described spondylolisthesis in 1839, and described three years later acute yellow atrophy of the liver, sometimes referred to as Rokitansky's disease. He also described traction diverticulum of the esophagus, amyloid of the kidney, multilocular ovarian cysts, and emphysema and differentiated lobar from lobular pneumonia. Rokitansky was one of the men of science who created the new Vienna School of Medicine and made the Austrian capital a center of medical research and study.

Rokitansky was born in Königgrätz, Bohemia, studied medicine at Prague, and received his MD degree from the University of Vienna when he was 24. He was made Director of the Pathological Institute in 1832 and two years later became a professor. The University of Vienna appointed him Dean of the Medical Faculty in 1849 and Rector of the University a year later.

Rokitansky's four volumes of the *Handbuch der pathologischen Anatomie* were issued over a five-year period. The first appeared in 1849 and propounded the fanciful humoral theory in connection with "crases" and "dyscrases." This was omitted in subsequent editions.

In 1878, Rokitansky died of a heart ailment in Vienna. His portrait appears on Austrian postage stamps (Scott Nos. B158 and 592) issued in 1937 and 1954, the latter to mark the 150th anniversary of his birth. Historically, Rokitansky's contribution was enormous, yet submerged by subsequent discoveries.—Mirt, J. A., Kyle, R. A., and Shampo, M. A.

DEVELOPMENT OF
RADIOTHERAPY AND
PHYSICAL THERAPY
IN CUBA

Francisco Dominguez Roldan (1864-1942), Cuban radiologist, served both the medical profession and his country with distinction for a half century. He studied medicine in Cuba, France, and Spain, and after receiving his MD degree in 1890, he began practice in Havana. In 1907, he introduced radiotherapy, then in its infancy, in Cuba.

Roldan's early medical career was during the period when the Cubans were engaged in a struggle for independence from Spain. He served as a colonel in the liberation forces which, in 1898, with the aid of the United States, succeeded in obtaining freedom from Spain. A republic was established in 1902. In later years, he served in public capacities. As Secretary of Education, he was influential in raising the literacy of Cubans.

A 4c postage stamp (Scott No. 591) issued in 1958 bears his portrait and honors him as one of Cuba's great physicians.—Mirt, J. A.

DISCOVERY OF
MALARIA ORGANISMS
IN MOSQUITO

Ronald Ross (1857-1932) was born in Almora, Northwest Province of India, in 1857 and was educated in England. His early interests were mathematics and literature. He became a medical student at St. Bartholomew's Hospital where his career was undistinguished and showed no aptitude for clinical work. He entered the Indian Medical Service in 1881 as an obedient son but spent most of his time working on higher mathematics, writing poetry and a novel.

He returned to England after seven years and studied bacteriology with E. E. Klein. Subsequently, he met Manson, who interested him in malaria. Ross returned to India, and after he had examined more than 1,000 mosquitoes, he found malarial organisms in the stomach of an Anopheles mosquito. The day of this discovery (Aug. 20, 1897) has been called Mosquito Day. He subsequently showed that malaria could be transferred from bird to bird by mosquitoes which had been fed on malaria-infected birds.

Ross returned to England, where he was a lecturer and demonstrator in tropical medicine and tropical pathology in the School of Tropical Medicine at the University of Liverpool.

Believing that he was not given proper credit for his discoveries, Ross became disconsolate. However, various scientists supported his priorities, and he subsequently received the Nobel Prize in Medicine in 1902. He continued working in the field of tropical diseases and ultimately became the director of the Ross Institute. He died on Sept. 16, 1932, and was honored on two Swedish stamps (Scott Nos. 617, 619) of the Nobel Prize issue of 1962.—Kyle, R. A., and Shampo, M. A.

INVESTIGATOR OF
INFECTIOUS DISEASES

Émile Roux (1853-1933) was born on Dec. 17, 1853, at Confolens, Charente, France. He began his medical studies at Clermont-Ferrand and studied under Emile Duclaux, who introduced him to Pasteur in 1878. He had a leading role in the work of Pasteur on anthrax and rabies. Later, he reported on the passage of the rabies virus along the nerves and on the pathology of experimental tetanus. Nocard and Roux first introduced glycerin agar as a culture medium for the tubercule bacilli. They also were the first to demonstrate the virulence of saliva of dogs infected with rabies. Roux studied the viricidal action of ether on the rabies virus, which action played an important role in vaccination.

Roux and Yersin discovered diphtheria toxin, and after von Behring's demonstration of diphtheria antitoxin, Roux was the first to use the horse for production of antitoxin. He and his colleagues worked out the mode of preparation and dosage of the antitoxin and in 1894, on the basis of their experience in 300 cases, reported that it was of great value in prophylaxis and therapy.

Roux became Director of the Pasteur Institute in 1904 and devoted the remainder of his life to administration at the Institute and to the stimulation of others to research. He would not allow his name to be attached to younger men's work, so that it is impossible to tell which contributions he made in the monumental works developed by the Institute.

Roux was an excellent teacher and began a course of bacteriology in 1889 which attracted more than 3,000 pupils from all over the world.

The last 30 years of his life, he suffered from chronic pulmonary tuberculosis. He was thin and emaciated, and was unable to tolerate cold. He was always seen in a long pellerine and woolen muffler. His diet consisted primarily of bread and soup, and he lived on 80c a day. Roux never married and lived in the hospital. He gave all of his prize money to the Pasteur Institute, keeping virtually nothing for himself. He died on Nov. 3, 1933, and after a national funeral was buried in the garden of the Pasteur Institute. He was honored philatelically by France (Scott No. B289) in 1954.—Kyle, R. A., and Shampo, M. A.

MUSICIAN, THEOLOGIAN, PHYSICIAN

Although Albert Schweitzer (1875-1965) appears best known today as a physician, perhaps history will place him on higher pinnacles in his two earlier professions, in both of which he excelled.

Alsatian by birth, Schweitzer early became famous in the musical world by his writings on Johann Sebastian Bach, whom he styled musician-poet in his 1905 biography. His writings had marked influence on the modern estimate of Bach's music for which Schweitzer had great admiration. Although not a composer, Schweitzer was the most accomplished organist of his day and a counsellor on organ building to many European countries.

Meanwhile Schweitzer's theological interests developed into a second career which found him a teacher of religion at Strasbourg, and author of "The Quest of the Historical Jesus," which has been described as a "life of the lives" of Christ. In reality this was a serious effort to extract from countless biographies that which was historically supported by external historical data on the life of Jesus.

From this point, Schweitzer's zeal to contribute to the welfare of man demanded, in his mind, the study of medicine, begun in 1905, and coming to fruition when he established the hospital at Lambaréné in French Equatorial Africa in 1913. He spent the greater part of his remaining life at the hospital, leaving it only for tours of organ concerts, the proceeds from which went to support his missionary hospital.

As physician, Schweitzer was priest and practitioner, and introduced his concept of "reverence for life" into all his work. Scientific medicine, with its feverish advances, left him in the rear ranks late in life, but the vitality of his effort never diminished. He was awarded the Nobel Peace Prize in 1952, and is shown here on a Gabon airmail stamp of 1960 (Scott No. C1).—Fite, G. L.

PUERPERAL FEVER

Motherhood is safer today because a Hungarian, Ignace Semmelweis (1818-1865), a graduate of the University of Vienna Medical School, worked against terrific opposition to prove to the world that the lives of mothers were being sacrificed because of poor hospital sanitation.

Semmelweis was appalled by the high maternal mortality rate from childbirth fever at the Vienna Lying-in Hospital. In 1847, he concluded that infection was spread by medical personnel. He introduced the practice of disinfecting hands. The death rate was lowered, yet despite this accomplishment, his theories were not generally accepted by medical authorities.

He returned to Budapest where the reception was equally cool. In 1865, he was taken to an insane asylum where he shortly developed gangrene from an infected finger wound sustained at a recent gynecological operation. He died in a few days, a victim of blood poisoning which he had discovered as identical to the puerperal fever he had sought to exterminate by antisepsis.

In the days to follow, Pasteur and Lister were to prove that the theories of Semmelweis had been correct. Semmelweis has been honored philatelically a number of times. Austria honored him on a stamp (Scott No. 746) issued in 1965 on the centenary of his death.—Mirt, J. A.

DIAGNOSIS VS TREATMENT

The so-called "Second Vienna School of Medicine" which prevailed in the middle of the 19th century produced some of Europe's greatest physicians. Among these was Josef Skoda (1805-1881), a therapeutic nihilist who was more interested in arriving at a diagnosis than in the treatment of a disease.

Like so many great physicians, Skoda's early education was in academic fields rather than in medicine. Born in Pilsen, Bohemia, he studied for the ministry, then turned his attention to mathematics and physics. And with the financial aid of affluent friends, he studied medicine.

Skoda received his MD degree from the University of Vienna in 1831. A year after his graduation, he affiliated with the famous *Allgemeine Krankenhaus.* His treatise, *Auscultation and Percussion* (1839), laid the foundation for modern physical diagnosis. His name is associated with several physical signs in the examination of the chest. He became a professor of medicine at the University of Vienna in 1847, and maintained that medical students should have direct observation of the sick. Breaking tradition, he lectured in German rather than in Latin.

Skoda, a bachelor, suffered from gout and died of heart disease, and as an early "pathfinder" in medicine, he left the beaten tracks to seek new horizons. He has been honored postally on a stamp (Scott No. B159) of the set honoring famous physicians issued by Austria in 1937.
—Mirt, J. A.

THEOLOGIAN
AND SCIENTIST

Emanuel Swedenborg (1688-1772), Swedish theologian and scientist, is best known for his religious and philosophical deductions. In the chronicles of his active career, most of the biographies fail to note that he was also a researcher in medicine.

Swedenborg was born Emanuel Swedberg, son of a Stockholm bishop. He studied at the University of Upsala, Sweden, and then traveled abroad for four years. In 1716, he was named assessor of mines by Charles XII of Sweden. When he was ennobled three years later, he changed his name to Swedenborg and took a prominent place in the House of Peers.

He was an extremely diligent worker, a keen observer, and an unprejudiced man of research, establishing himself as an outstanding pioneer in the knowledge of cerebral localization. He contributed new knowledge on the cortex of the brain with his observations made during the years 1734-1745.

Although the concepts of the cerebral cortex as the seat of mental abilities had to some degree already been covered, Swedenborg seems to have arrived at his conclusions in part by experiments on animals. Yet his main research was by recording and comparing the findings of a large number of autopsies at universities in Sweden, England, and elsewhere in Europe.

Swedenborg localized hemiplegia to the brain and paraplegia to the spinal cord, and arrived at a conception of the function of the basal ganglia. He believed that this region collected different impulses, and initiated automatic movements. He also is said to have been familiar with the importance of corpora quadrigemina for the movement of the pupils, and to have investigated the central canal of the spinal cord.

His activities as theologian increased at the same time, and in 1743 he claimed that he had received a Divine commission to disclose the spiritual sense of the Scripture which differed in many respects with existing beliefs. He died in London within an hour of the time he had predicted for himself and was buried in the Cathedral of Upsala. The New Church, or New Jerusalem Church, which accepts his philosophy and theology, was organized in London in 1783.

Swedenborg was honored postally by Sweden (Scott Nos. 264-267) in 1936 on the 250th anniversary of his birth.—Mirt, J. A.

EUROPEAN INTERNIST

Holland-born Gerhard Freiherr van Swieten (1700-1772) started Vienna's Medical School on its road to fame. Swieten was a pupil of Boerhaave at the University of Leyden, Holland, and gained renown as a physician in his native land and throughout other countries of Europe.

His work attracted the attention of Queen Maria Theresa of Austria and she appointed him as physician in ordinary. She delegated him to reorganize education, including medicine. This he did with the aid of other distinguished physicians. A new Academy of Science was erected, training schools for midwives were founded, the first veterinary college and foundling hospital were established, and plans laid for the *Allgemeine Krankenhaus,* which became the most famous medical teaching institution in all Europe. He was knighted by the Queen.

Swieten's name is associated with liquor Swietanii, a corrosive sublimate solution used in the treatment of syphilis. His portrait is seen on a stamp (Scott No. B156) from the set of famous Austrian physicians issued in 1937.
—Mirt, J. A.

FERMENTATION AS THE PROCESS OF LIFE

An insatiable curiosity about form and mechanism was the keynote to the supremacy of Dutch medicine in the late 17th century. Franciscus de le Boe, or Sylvius (1614-1672) contributed to this leadership not only as an outstanding teacher but also by his scientific findings which advanced medical knowledge.

Sylvius (not to be confused with the French pedant, Jacques Dubois, also known as Sylvius), was born in Hanau, Prussia and received his medical education at the University of Basel. He studied further in Paris, developed a large practice in Amsterdam, and lectured on botany and anatomy in Leiden. In 1658, he became a professor of medicine at the University of Leiden, a position he held until his death in 1672.

A handsome, witty man, with exquisite manners, Sylvius, as was the case with most teachers of his time, had an elaborate system. This was that fermentation is the process of life. It changes one thing into another and results in the formation of acids and alkalies. When these are in balance, the body is well. These concepts are known today as acidosis and alkalosis.

The doctrines of Sylvius gained credence because the master was able to demonstrate the successful results of their application on patients at the bedside, a clinic of 12 beds having been set aside for him in 1663 for practical teaching purposes. He had a good concept of ductless glands and of the thermal and tactile senses. Sylvius produced works on anatomy and described parts of the brain which now bear his name. He was honored philatelically (Scott No. B95) by The Netherlands in 1937.—Mirt, J. A.

DEVELOPMENT OF
MODERN SURGERY

Octave Terrillon (1844-1895), French surgeon, was a pioneer in asepsis. As early as 1882, he used boiling water to sterilize surgical instruments. He wrote a monograph on this technique in 1892.

Terrillon received his MD degree from the University of Paris in 1873, later serving as a professor of surgery at the Salpêtrière and Lourcine hospitals in Paris. He developed "Terrillon's Operation" which used an elastic ligature in the removal of hydatids.

It is ironic that a bacterial infection should lead to the death of Terrillon. During a surgical operation, pus squirted into his eye. The resultant pyemia was fatal.

A postage stamp issued by France (Scott No. 823) in 1957 bears his portrait, surgical instruments, microscope, and autoclave, with the inscription "creator of asepsis."—Mirt, J. A.

MEDICAL EDUCATION
IN SOUTH AMERICA

José Hipolito Unanue y Pavon (1755-1833), who prepared for the ministry, became one of the famous anatomists and medical educators in Peru. Interspersed in a career covering nearly a half century was more than a decade devoted to leadership in the liberation of Peru from Spanish control.

Unanue received his MD degree from San Marcos University in Lima. He became Professor of Anatomy in 1789. In 1810, he founded the San Fernando University, adding a College of Medicine in the following year.

In 1821, Peru declared its independence from Spain and eventually won its freedom. Unanue was a key figure in this movement and the subsequent establishment of a new republic. Among the posts he held in the new nation were those of Prime Minister, President of the Congress, and Minister of Justice. He is honored in the Pan-American Union's Hall of Heroes in Washington.

Unanue, a member of medical organizations in the United States and Europe, was instrumental in furthering medical education in South America. He was honored postally by Peru (Scott No. C150) in 1958 on the 400th anniversary of the founding of San Marcos University, his alma mater.—Mirt, J. A.

RENAISSANCE ANATOMIST

The teachings of Claudius Galen (ca. 130—ca. 200) dominated medicine for 14 centuries. But in five years the Belgian-born Andreas Vesalius (1514-1564) demonstrated many of the fallacies in Galenism.

Despite the bitter opposition from those clinging to the ancient theories, Vesalius raised the study of human anatomy to a science based on observation. His *De Humani Corporis Fabrica* (1543) reflected his courage of independent thought in keeping with the resurgent spirit of the Renaissance. The "Fabrica" is an elegant and artistic presentation of the human figure.

Vesalius, born in Brussels, became a student of medicine at the University of Paris where he was indoctrinated in Galenic anatomy. He acquired considerable knowledge by surreptitiously visiting old cemeteries and the gallows where he gathered an abundance of dissecting material. This activity also resulted in his banishment from France.

Vesalius journeyed to Switzerland, then to Italy. He received his MD degree from the University of Padua on Dec. 5, 1537. On the following day, after demonstrating a dissection, he was appointed a professor of surgery.

After working arduously on his dissections, Vesalius expressed his revolutionary views on anatomy in *De Humani Corporis Fabrica et Epitome,* a companion piece. Many of his contemporaries criticized him; others supported him. However, he abandoned teaching for a more lucrative practice.

In 1544, Vesalius became court physician to Charles V of Spain and 12 years later to the successor, Philip II.

Later, he undertook a pilgrimage to the Holy Land. On his return journey, he is believed to have been shipwrecked on a small Greek island where he died.

Vesalius was the first physician to break with tradition regarding anatomy and to write of it from observation. He freed medical science from the fetters of Galenism and stimulated others through example to greater strides in anatomic research in later centuries. Several anatomical structures, including sesamoid bones, bronchial mucous glands, and inguinal ligaments are named after him.

Belgium, in 1964, commemorated the 400th anniversary of his death with a postage stamp (Scott No. 570) showing Vesalius explaining a dissected arm.—Mirt, J. A.

EPIDEMIOLOGIST

Jean Hyacinthe Vincent (1862-1950) was born on Dec. 22, 1862, in Bordeaux, France, and graduated in medicine from the University of Bordeaux in 1888. He entered the French Army Service and subsequently joined the Val-de-Grâce Military Hospital in 1896, ultimately to become a professor of epidemiology there in 1912. In 1894, he isolated *Nocardia madurae (actinomyces madurae)*, which is one of the organisms that causes madura foot. Two years later he discovered *Borrelia vincentii* and *Fusobacterium plauti vincentii*, which he found associated with hospital gangrene. Later, he demonstrated these two organisms in ulceromembranous stomatitis, which is known as Vincent's angina or trench mouth.

Vincent introduced new methods of preparing typhoid-paratyphoid vaccine which were very valuable in World War I, and was instrumental in making typhoid vaccination compulsory for French troops—thus significantly decreasing the mortality rate from typhoid. He also made important contributions to the etiology and pathogenesis of tetanus.

In addition to his work related to bacteriology, Vincent authored papers on occipital neuralgia, the relationship of thyroid disease and rheumatism, Graves' disease, scleroderma, and meningitis.

He died on Nov. 23, 1950, and was honored philatelically on the centenary of his birth by a French stamp (Scott No. B364) issued in 1962. Kyle, R. A., and Shampo, M. A.

CELLULAR
PATHOLOGY

Small in stature, Rudolf Virchow (1821-1902) was a giant in the field of science. He developed the importance of cellular response in pathology. The fruits of his research earned him recognition as the founder of the school of medical science which concerns itself with the cause, the process, and the results of disease—pathology.

Virchow, born in Schivelbein, Germany, received his MD degree from the University of Berlin in 1843. Fifteen years later he demolished the 20-century-old theory that four cardinal body fluids, or humours, had a relationship to health and disease. As a pupil of Schleiden and of Schwamm, he placed the seat of disease in the body's essential unit—the cell. This concept of cellular pathology was of monumental importance because it gave medicine a new basis for understanding disease. It also established a new basis for therapy.

Virchow is said to have challenged Bismarck to a duel while investigating archaeology and histology. He provoked major reforms in sanitation and public health controls which resulted in part from his report on typhus fever —a masterpiece of medical facts.

He described leukemia, embolism, thrombosis, myelin, amyloid, and leprosy. As a professor of pathology at the University of Berlin from 1857 until his death in 1902 from heart failure, he became acknowledged as a great teacher. He is remembered not only through his own works but those of many celebrated pupils; his lectures on pathology and malignant tumors are classics.

Virchow was a humanist, serving as the people's representative in the German Reichstag, Prussian Diet, and Berlin Council. He supervised the erection of public hospitals. At his death he was accorded a state funeral. He was honored philatelically (Scott No. 520) by the German Democratic Republic in 1950.—Mirt, J. A., Kyle, R. A., and Shampo, M. A.

REGIONAL ANESTHESIA

Alexander Vishnevski (1874-1948) was born in Dagestan, Russia and graduated from Kazan University in 1904. After graduation, he studied anatomy and pathology. He believed in conservation of tissue in surgical procedures and was noted for his work on reconstructive surgery. He applied balsam oil dressing after cleansing wounds. He headed the surgical clinic of VIEM (All Union Institute of Experimental Medicine).

Vishnevski developed a method of tissue infiltration of procaine hydrochloride (Novacaine) in saline (Novacaine blockade), and this led to its application in cervical, lumbar, and sacral nerve blocks. He worked as a laboratory assistant at the Pasteur Institute in Paris where he was associated with Metchnikoff. Vishnevski also did research on the physiology of intestinal innervation.

He was awarded the Cross of Lenin and the Order of the Red Banner of Labor. The Surgical Institute of the Academy of Medical Sciences in Moscow was named in his honor. His portrait can be seen on a Russian stamp (Scott No. 2936) issued in 1964.—Kyle, R. A., and Shampo, M. A.

AUSTRIAN NEUROLOGIST INVENTS FEVER THERAPY

Julius Wagner-Jauregg (1857-1940), neurologist and psychiatrist, was awarded the 1927 Nobel Prize in Medicine for his discovery of a method of treating general paralysis of the insane with fever. His procedure involved the injection of malaria germs and subsequently the curing of the malaria by the use of quinine.

Wagner-Jauregg was a graduate of the University of Vienna, class of 1880, and specialized in mental diseases. He was appointed director of the Provincial Hospital's Psychiatric Clinic, Vienna, in 1893. From his extensive research in thyroid deficiency came the use of iodized salt in the treatment and prevention of cretinism and endemic goiter.

He was honored philatelically (Scott No. 615) by Austria in 1957 on the centenary of his birth.—Mirt, J. A.

REPUBLIQUE·FRANÇAISE

WIDAL
1862-1929

12ᶠ

POSTES

EARLY DIAGNOSIS OF
TYPHOID FEVER

Georges Fernand Isidore Widal (1862-1929), French pathologist, and bacteriologist, was an important influence in French medicine in the early 20th century. A Socratic teacher, he combined a zeal for investigation with clinical wisdom and experimental precision. He contributed much toward making medicine an exact science.

Widal was born in Dellys, Algiers, the son of a physician, and studied medicine at the University of Paris. He received his doctorate at the age of 27 with his thesis on clinical manifestations of streptococcal infections.

In 1894, he was appointed to the professional group at the University of Paris. Two years later, after a joint study with André Chantemesse (1851-1919) they reported an agglutination test for typhoid fever using a living agglutinable culture of the typhoid bacillus as an antigen. By this method, typhoid fever could be recognized almost instantly by observing microscopically the action of a patient's serum on a culture of Eberth's bacillus. The test is now performed by using H and O antigens.

The United States Army in 1909 began the huge experiment of vaccinating its soldiers against typhoid after the method advocated by the two Frenchmen. As a result, the Army was freed of typhoid.

In 1910, Widal was appointed Professor of Internal Pathology, and seven years later he succeeded to the Chair of Clinical Medicine. He separated types of nephritis, studied hemolytic anemias, and paroxysmal hemoglobinuria produced by cold. He also discussed hereditary spherocytosis, cytodiagnosis of exudates, anaphylaxis, urticaria, and hemolytic crisis.

Widal received the highest French scientific honor—membership in the "Institute," and the highest civilian recognition, the Grand Cross of the Legion of Honour. France placed his portrait on a 12-franc postage stamp (Scott No. 866) issued in 1958.—Mirt, J. A.

CAMPAIGN FOR
PURE FOODS AND DRUGS

Today's stringent pure foods and drugs laws are a memorial to a Fellow of the American Medical Association. Harvey W. Wiley (1844-1930), a graduate of Indiana Medical College, carried on a relentless, militant campaign against adulterated foods and harmful drugs. Passage of the Pure Food and Drug Act of 1906 was the result of his efforts.

After receiving his MD degree in 1871, Wiley took a two-year postgraduate course in chemistry at Harvard University. He taught for 10 years before becoming head of the Bureau of Chemistry, United States Department of Agriculture in 1883. It was in that position that he saw how the health of the public was being affected by adulteration of foods and drugs.

Wiley served the USDA for another six years after the passage of the Pure Foods and Drugs Act, and set up an efficient enforcement machinery. The last 16 years of his life were spent in the chemical field and in writing. He was honored by a stamp (Scott No. 1080) issued by the United States on the 50th anniversary of the Pure Food and Drug Act.—Mirt, J. A.

FROM WITCHCRAFT TO PSYCHIATRY

Johannes Wier or Weyer (1515-1588), also known as Wierus, was born in Grave on the Meuse in the Netherlands. He went to school at Hertogenbosch, and later studied under the guidance of H. C. Agrippa von Nettersheim, an opponent of sorcery and witchcraft who imbued Wier with the spirit of liberal humanism.

In 1534, Wier began the study of medicine at the University of Paris and then the University of Orleans, France, from which he graduated in 1537.

In 1545, he became City Physician of Arnheim, The Netherlands, and in 1550, personal court physician to William III, Duke of Jülich and Cleves.

Wier was a careful observer and clinician, and in his "Artzney Buch," he described many diseases and their treatment. His main effort, however, was directed against the persecution of witches, especially after the book *Mallea Maleficarum* written by the Dominican Inquisitors Sprenger and Kraemner initiated a veritable mass extinction of men, women, and children by the thousands through torture.

Wier saw this demoniacal world filled with mentally ill people and recommended medical treatment. In 1563, Wier wrote his *De Praestigiis Daemonun* in which he applied his knowledge in their defense. When William III became mentally ill, Wier himself was accused of witchcraft, and he had to flee to Tecklenburg near Osnabruck, where he died on Feb. 24, 1588.

Broadly regarded as the father of psychiatry, Wier was philatelically honored in 1960 by a Netherlands stamp (Scott No. 384) issued to focus attention on World Mental Health Year.—Shampo, M. A., and Kyle, R. A.

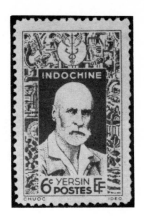

RESEARCH INTO THE
BLACK PLAGUE

Impressed by the new vistas in medicine opened up by Louis Pasteur in the last quarter of the 19th century, Swiss-born Alexandre Jean Emile Yersin (1863-1943) decided to take up bacteriology as a career.

Yersin received his MD degree from the University of Paris in 1887. He became associated with Pierre Paul Émile Roux (1853-1933), French bacteriologist, in experimental work. In 1888, the two confirmed Pasteur's finding of the pathogenic effects of a clear filtrate on specific organisms in chicken cholera.

That same year, they proved the existence of a soluble diphtheria toxin by passing the culture through a porcelain filter. And in the following year they pointed out the danger of diphtheria convalescents as carriers.

In 1893, the reports of bubonic plague in Hong Kong aroused Yersin's scientific curiosity. He went there and succeeded in isolating the offending organism, *Pasteurella pestis.* The Japanese bacteriologist, Shibusaburo Kitasato (1852-1931), working independently, did likewise at the same time. Yersin developed a prophylactic serum in 1897, but this serum proved unreliable.

He was honored philatelically (Scott Nos. 234-236) on stamps issued by Indo-China in 1943.—Mirt, J. A.

UKRAINIAN EPIDEMIOLOGIST

Kirill Danilowitsch Zabolotny (1866-1929) was born on Dec. 16, 1866, in Trchebotarewka, Ukraine. He received his MD degree from the University of Kiev in 1894.

He became a professor of bacteriology in St. Petersburg in 1898, where he demonstrated that cholera vaccine was effective taken orally. He organized epidemiological departments in medical schools in Russia and became the Director of the Institute for Experimental Medicine.

Zabolotny was active in many international congresses on epidemic diseases and wrote a textbook in 1927 entitled *Fundamentals of Epidemiology*. He died in Kiev on Dec. 15, 1929, and was postally honored by Russia (Scott No. 3190) in 1966.–Kyle, R. A., and Shampo,M. A.

OPHTHALMOLOGIST
DEVELOPS
UNIVERSAL LANGUAGE

Lazarus Ludwig Zamenhof (1859-1917) was born in Bylostok, Russian Poland, on Dec. 15, 1859, and studied medicine at the University of Poland where he received his degree in 1882.

While practicing ophthalmology in Warsaw, he became interested in a universal language in the hope of uniting the world with a common bond. In 1887, he created Esperanto, meaning "hopeful tongue" and published its rules and syntax. This new language soon aroused international interest because of its simplicity and the hope of universal communication. Many international congresses were held, and the language grew in popularity. Zamenhof died in Warsaw on April 4, 1917, and has been honored philatelically as an educator.

Strange as it seems, Esperanto is used to a greater extent than is realized. More than 100 periodicals are published in Esperanto, and congresses and conventions are held frequently to foster its use.

Examples in Esperanto and in English are cited:
Sur neutrala lingva fundamento,
Komprenate unu la alian,
La poploj faros enkonsento
Uno grandan rondon familian.

———

On a neutral lingual foundation,
Each understanding the other,
The peoples shall form in agreement
One great family circle.

Many stamps have been issued in Zamenhof's honor. Hungary (Scott No. C171) honored him on a stamp issued in 1957, commemorating the 70th anniversary of Esperanto.—Shampo, M. A., and Kyle, R. A.

INDEX

213

Nobel Prizes
These were first awarded in 1901, in the five categories for Peace, Chemistry, Physics, Physiology and Medicine, and Literature.

In some years the prize has been divided among two or three individuals. Marie Curie stands alone in having been given awards in more than one category. In 1903 the award in physics was shared by Mme. Curie, her husband, and Becquerel.

Peace
Dunant	1901
Schweitzer	1952

Chemistry
Curie	1911

Physics
Röntgen	1901
Becquerel	1903
Curie	1903
Fermi	1938

Physiology and Medicine

von Behring	1901		Laveran	1907
Ross	1902		Ehrlich	1908
Finsen	1903		Metchnikoff	1908
Pavlov	1904		Kocher	1909
Koch	1905		Richet	1913
Golgi	1906		Wagner-Jauregg	1927
Ramón y Cajal	1906		Nicolle	1928
			Landsteiner	1930
			Egas Moniz	1949